The Price Guide to
JEWELLERY

3000 B.C.–1950 A.D.

by Michael Poynder

Antique Collectors' Club

Frontispiece

A unique range of diamonds illustrating their immense variety of colour.

(De Beers Consolidated Mines Ltd.)

Published for the Antique Collectors' Club by the Antique Collectors' Club Ltd.

Printed in England by the Antique Collectors' Club Ltd., Church Street, Woodbridge, Suffolk

Front Cover Caption

Left to right, top to bottom
Victorian hardstone (agate) cameo in an 18ct., gold frame, c.1860. £800 — £1,200
Mid-Victorian blue enamel and gold scroll brooch set with diamonds, c.1845.
£1,800 — £2,300
Victorian gold piqué and tortoiseshell 'scallop shell' shaped brooch. *£200 — £250*
Victorian turquoise and gold scroll brooch with pendant locket, c.1865. *£500 — £700*
Oval 'Roman' style brooch, classical revival perod in 19th century, of gold and lapis lazuli.
£500 — £750
Georgian padlock of gold and blue enamel and real half pearls, c.1825. *£300 — £400*
Art nouvean enamel and gold brooch with pearl drop, *pliqué-à-jour* technique, c.1900.
£1,500 — £2,000
Gold, amethyst and pearl pendant locket, c.1880. *£1,800 — £2,200*
Surrounding the photograph, a garnet and gold necklace. English, c.1820. *£1,400 — £2,000*

Acknowledgements

I wish to thank Marie Mills of Thesaurus in Antiquarius, Flood Street, London S.W.3, and my secretary, Elizabeth Ashley Cooper, FGA, for their immense help, enthusiasm and knowledge without which this book could not have been completed.

I would like to offer my thanks to the following businesses and individuals, listed alphabetically, who have allowed me to photograph their stock and given me the benefit of their vast combined knowledge.

Antiquarius: Tony & Sara, Thesaurus
                 The Purple Shop, Stall M1, Bellamy
                 John Taylor, Anne Tan Antiques Ltd. Chimera

Armour Winston Ltd.   Harvey & Gore Ltd.
Asprey & Co. Ltd.   Hennell Ltd.
The Assay Office of Great Britain   Institute of Geological Sciences
B. Barnett Ltd.   The Jewel House Ltd.
Benjamin Jewellery Ltd.   Landsberg & Son Ltd.
Bernard Silver Ltd.   W. Lewis Ltd.
Catherine Berry   Liberty & Co. Ltd.
N. Bloom & Son Ltd.   Lynda Perkins Antiques
Boucheron Ltd.   Manfred Seymour Ltd.
Peter Brady (Photographer)   Albert Middlemiss (Christie's)
Eric Bruton   G. Music & Sons Ltd.
Cameo Corner Ltd.   James R. Ogden & Sons Ltd.
Cartier Ltd.   Richard Ogden Ltd.
Christie Manson & Woods (Christie's) S.J. Phillips Ltd.
Collingwood of Conduit St. Ltd.   S.J. Rose Ltd.
A.C. Cooper Ltd.   C. Shapland
Cultured Pearl Co. Ltd.   Sotheby Parke Bernet (Sotheby's)
De Beers Consolidated Mines Ltd.   Sotheby Parke Bernet (Hong Kong)
Richard Digby   Tessiers Ltd.
Richard Falkiner   Vogue Magazine
M. Hakim Antiques   Wartski Ltd.
Hancock & Co. Ltd.

Contents

Index to page nos. of colour plates

Introduction

In compiling this book I have only been able to give an idea of the style and quality of jewellery over the centuries. The book is, after all, a Price Guide. But, in order that readers might appreciate jewellery more, I have tried to fill in as much background information as possible in terms of origins, technical details, mounting and setting, and the sentiment that attaches to small things of great value.

Man has adorned himself and his women for thousands of years but few pieces of jewellery are ever the same, and no single stone is identical to another in terms of colour, clarity and shape. Therefore, each piece of jewellery must be appreciated or rejected in its own right. Also, no two jewellers will evaluate the same piece of jewellery in the same way. Experience and knowledge will always vary with the individual, as will personal taste. Today, fashion changes at alarming speed. Five years ago art deco jewellery was unsaleable but is now keenly bought and highly priced, particularly named "craft" jewellery. At the moment Georgian and Victorian diamond work is out of favour and is comparatively cheap, even at auction. Yet, the best pieces of jewellery have appreciated gradually over the years and this is brought about by the rising prices in the salerooms, which we must accept as a yardstick since prices under the hammer reflect the general trend of fashion and taste.

The prices quoted as a guide in this book echo the prices being asked in various retail businesses in England. None of these estimates include or allow for Value Added Tax (VAT) in any way whatsoever. VAT is variable and all jewellery is subject to VAT in one form or another. The machinations of the tax are so complicated that it is not within the scope of this book to teach its workings. However, I would mention that non-residents of the United Kingdom do not have to pay VAT, providing the piece is exported within three months of purchase.

Prices will vary from shop to shop. Obviously if you shop in Bond Street and buy your jewellery from world-renowned firms with expensive premises and a large staff, then you must expect to pay for the privilege, but rest assured that you are paying for some of the best craftsmanship in the world. However, in the last few years antique markets have sprung up serving the public and the antiques trade, with many individual stall-holders dealing in jewellery, silver and objets d'art. This has expanded interest and knowledge in all facets of antiques, and allows members of the public wishing to buy and sell to do so without feeling embarrassed at taking minor objects to an awe-inspiring shop. The "trade" has therefore become much less formal and this must be a good thing for everybody.

I mention these aspects of the business at some length since they are borne out in the contents of the book, where 95% of the pieces shown are, or have been, on sale in particular shops, or have passed through the salerooms within the last few years. Many similar pieces from different shops would seem to have varying prices, and this illustrates the difference between buying from the top of the ladder in the West End and from the bottom in the market stalls. Therefore, I have shown a price against each piece relevant to the shop concerned and within the range of the price asked, but not what I myself think it is worth.

The prices are within a bracket which the private individual might expect to pay when buying from a retail business, and should not be taken as a guide to what he might be offered when selling. Nobody is in business for charity and you, the individual, must expect a jeweller to make a profit, so the amount you will be offered will vary with the experience and personal taste of the purchaser. I remember being told by a respected member of the jewellery trade that the most important person in the business is the man who says: "I will give you..." and is prepared to put his money on the table.

A word on insurance. Every week there are hundreds of burglaries, and jewellery is the prime target. Please bring your insurance up to date every two or three years to keep in line with inflation. You should not be charged more than a nominal fee if you use the same jeweller who did your original valuation, and if you go to the same shop regularly your revaluation will probably be done free. Members of the British Antique Dealers' Association (BADA), London and Provincial Antique Dealers' Association (LAPADA) and National Association of Goldsmiths (NAG) recommend initial charges of approximately 1% up to £3,000 and descending thereafter, according to total value or quantity of articles.

Finally as to the content of the book. It is arranged chronologically as far as possible in terms of both date and style. But many of the plates are mixed as it would have been impossible to move hundreds of individual pieces from shop to shop to achieve a concise plate. Time and security were against that. Also I have tried to relate the number of illustrations directly to the type of jewellery most readily available and the greatest number of plates to the most prolific period. Hence rings of the nineteenth century dominate the book whereas Anglo-Saxon jewellery is so rare that only one piece is illustrated, yet that is a ring!

Michael Poynder
June 1976

Ancient Jewellery

A considerable amount of jewellery from the Ancient World has survived. Because virtually all ancient peoples had a materialistic concept of the next world, the rich provided their dead with status symbols to impress those they would meet in the next world. Due to the fact that gold is nearly immutable, and may be recovered in a pristine condition, while objects buried at the same time have decayed, most surviving ancient jewellery is gold. Much ancient jewellery is of such a flimsy construction that we must assume that most of it was supplied by the undertaker rather than the jeweller although this is not always the case, particularly with such personal objects as rings.

Gold was mined in the Wicklow Hills in Ireland in prehistoric times, and in the Iberian Peninsula in the second millennium BC.

Egyptian gold is very rare and for the most part impure, usually being alloyed with silver. Gold was relatively rare in Europe until the end of the 4th century BC when Alexander the Great captured the Persian King Darius's Treasury, which provided the main source of gold in the West for the next few centuries.

The Greeks preferred silver or electrum, a natural alloy of gold and silver, as they said it resembled the light of the moon rather than the heat of the sun, and it is only with the development of the Hellenistic Empire after the death of Alexander the Great (323 BC), that gold became relatively common. During the Ptolemaic period (late 4th century BC), gold became increasingly popular and most jewellery was made in Alexandria and Carthage until the end of the Roman Empire.

The Etruscans furnished the tombs of their illustrious dead more sumptuously than most races. However, this was mainly with bronzes and furnishings. Etruscan jewellery, particularly gold, is very rare indeed although it is now extensively faked. This work is usually obvious but there are some deceptive pieces.

Most Roman jewellery came from the Eastern Empire (modern Turkey) and, continuing the Ptolemaic tradition, from North Africa.

The advent of Christianity as the official religion of the Romans under Constantine the Great, at the beginning of the 4th century AD, did not interrupt the manufacture of jewellery, which continued until the Dark Ages. Then gold more or less disappeared from the European scene with the exception of the loot of the Vikings towards the end of the period. Europe remained largely devoid of gold until the mid-14th century, and the supply increased about one hundred and fifty years later with the discovery of the riches of the New World.

Much ancient jewellery is set with stones which were culled from all over the then known world. Hardstones came from as far away as the Red Sea, and gem stones were acquired from mysterious Central Asia along the silk route, which extended to China. The most common stones were the many varieties of agate, followed by garnets, mostly from the East. Diamonds make their appearance in a very few instances during the Roman period. These stones, presumably, came from North India, along with sapphires and the occasional ruby. Glass beads were extensively used, and there are accounts of Roman forgers of engraved gems using paste (glass).

The legal requirements of ownership gave rise to the use of seals from about 3000 BC and they were carved from various hardstones. Some archaic Greek seals of the 6th century BC are of scarab form and their backs are carved in relief. This eventually developed into the craft of cameo cutting which reached its zenith in the 1st century BC and it was not until the Renaissance that this exceptional level of craftsmanship was repeated.

(Christie's)

Plate 1

Northern Greek silver snake bracelet, 6th century BC. These bracelets are also found in gold
and would cost in the region of £5,000 — £8,000.
£1,000 — £1,500

(Christie's)

Plate 2

Greek pectoral (chest ornament) of gold repoussé work, Rhodes, 7th century BC.
£5,000 — £8,000

11

Beads are the simplest form of jewellery and are virtually impossible to date, as the stones involved do not decay. Consequently, beads which might have been of immemorial age, even in the Roman period, have been used again and again over the centuries. Certain shapes are distinctive of a period, but it is prudent to regard beads as timeless and their origins obscure because of their portability. Sometimes, beads and stones that have lain buried in the ground for a long time show surface etching that, to a practised eye, gives an indication of age. However, style and experience with ancient jewellery, particularly engraved gems, are the best guides to authenticity.

The designs are classical and occasional pieces of prehistoric jewellery have come down to us in the form of primitive and folk jewellery from the remoter parts of Europe and Asia. The designs of many pieces have hardly altered to this day. They are not imitations but evidence of a continuing tradition.

(Christie's)

Plate 3

Greek or Etruscan gold funerary wreath, made of fine gold leaf, 5th-3rd century BC. Funerary wreaths were usually made in laurel, ivory or oak leaf designs.
£5,000 — £10,000

Plate 4

Hellenistic gold medallion of Apollo, on a flexible plaited gold chain, 4th-3rd century BC.
£3,000 — £5,000
A pair of Greek Erotes earrings in gold, 4th-3rd century BC.
£2,000 — £3,000
Hellenistic gold fringe necklace on a flat plaited mesh chain, 3rd-2nd century BC
£5,000 — £8,000

All three pieces have been questioned and are possible reproductions — prices as genuine.

(Christie's)

Plate 5

Left to right, top to bottom
A pair of Greek gold earrings, designed as bulls' heads, threaded with glass beads, 3rd
century BC
£900 — £1,200
A pair of Greek gold earrings, designed as dolphins' heads, threaded with glass beads, 3rd
century BC. Dolphins' heads are much rarer than earrings with bulls' or lions' heads.
£900 — £1,200
Hellenistic style embossed gold medallion.
£1,500 — £2,500
A necklace of genuine Egyptian faïence scarabs on a modern Cairo work necklace,
suggesting the ancient style.
£1,000 — £2,000
A pair of traditional Islamic gold earrings.
£300 — £500

14

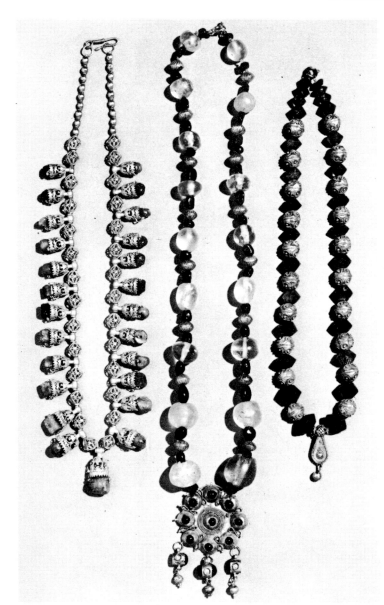

Plate 6

Left to right

A group of three bead necklaces, typical of what is available in Persia today. These necklaces are made up of assorted beads of any period back to about 3000 BC. There is no way of telling the age of beads as they are more or less indestructible and are frequently re-used, even if they have lain in a tomb for a millennium or more.

1. Emerald and aventurine quartz beads, typical traditional Islamic manufacture, short of definite evidence could be of any period.

£1,500 — £2,500

2. Garnet and crystal beads in gold with pendant.

£300 — £800

3. Hollow gold and emerald beads.

£300 — £800

(Christie's)

(Simone de Monbrison)

Plate 7

Egyptian gold necklace, from the New Kingdom period (1567-1085 BC). Note the
resemblance of design the work of the 19th century jewellery Giuliano bears to this example
of ancient jewellery.
£6,000 — £10,000

Plate 8

A necklace made up of Egyptian gold amulets and hardstone beads. Amulets usually sell for
between £80-£120 individually, and would originally have been bound in the mummy
wrappings.
£6,000 — £10,000

Plate 9

Egyptian necklace of faïence beads with gold palmette, fly and lotus pendants. Faïence disc beads of this type are particularly common from Egyptian tombs of virtually all dynasties, mainly from the 18th Dynasty (c. 1560-1320 BC) onwards, and are still reasonably obtainable from about £20 upwards, but are obviously considerably more expensive when there are gold additions.
£4,000 — £6,000

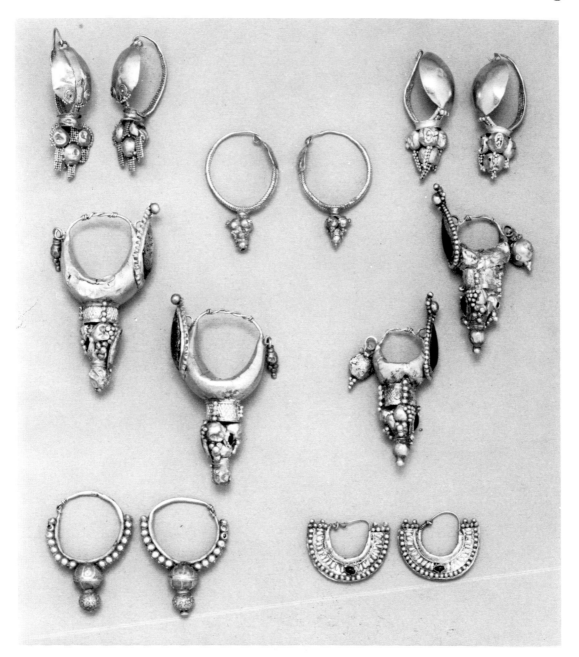

(Christie's)

Plate 10

A selection of gold earrings, mostly of complicated form, from Parthia (modern Persia), set
with pastes, c.1-500 AD.
£500 — £2,000 very variable

(Richard Falkiner)

Plate 11

Irish gold 'ribbon' torque (necklace), c.1200-600 BC.
£5,000 — £10,000

(Christie's)

Plate 12

Prehistoric Irish gold armlet, dating between 1000-400 BC. Dug up
in Cheshire. A section taken across the spiralling shows that this is
cruciform rather than the single spiral of the 'ribbon' torque.
£20,500 — £50,000 very rare

Plate 13

(Christie's)

Roman gold chain necklace with a high relief embossed medallion of the Head of Medusa,
2nd century AD.
£5,000 — £8,000

(Mrs. D. Papadimitriou)

Plate 14

Two fine Roman gold bracelets, 2nd century AD. The construction of the spiral is such that they
can be expanded slightly. Today, distorting them for wear is unwise as the metal, particularly
if silver, tends to have crystallised with the passage of time and this can result in their fracture.
£8,000 — £12,000 each

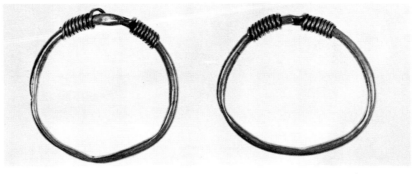

(Sotheby's)

Plate 15

Two Roman gold bracelets, 2nd/3rd century AD.
£6,000 — £8,000 each

Plate 16

A selection of Roman earrings, from the 1st-3rd centuries AD, all in gold, and some set with garnets or red pastes, faïence, amethysts or cornelians. If numbered from left to right, top to bottom, Nos. 4 and 5 are typical of early granulated patterns, No. 5 is probably Eastern Empire, and No. 9 incorporates stylised dolphins of the later Roman period of the 3rd century AD.

£3,000 — £4,000 per pair

(Christie's)

Plate 17

Byzantine gold pierced and engraved pendant and chain. The work on the pendant is typical Byzantine work of the period 4th-6th century AD. (Incidentally, this particular example has been stolen from its owner.)
£15,000 — £25,000

Plate 18

Byzantine solid gold cross on gold chain. A typical piece of Byzantine jewellery, more often found in bronze than in gold, 6th-7th century AD.

£3,000 — £5,000 much reduced in size

(J. Ogden)

Plate 19

Left
Garnet and gilt bronze 'fibula' or safety pin, North European 500-800 AD.

£5,000 — £10,000

Right
Spanish bronze belt buckle of Byzantine type, Mediterranean, c.500 AD.

£750 — £1,200

(Casper Fleming Collection)

Plate 20

Early 7th century, Frankish, circular gold brooch on bronze back, set with blue and red glass, malachite and shell.

£6,000 — £10,000

(J. Ogden)

(James R. Ogden Ltd.)

Plate 21

Top to bottom, left to right
Heavy rare Anglo-Saxon plain gold ring, 6th-7th century AD.
£5,000 — £8,000
Silver signet ring with crowned 'R', perhaps relating to Richard III, late 15th century.
£2,000 — £3,000
Bronze signet or merchant's ring, 16th century (usually gilt).
£550 — £1,000
Elizabethan gold memorial ring, 16th century, with white enamel skull with motto reading
'COGITA MORI'
£2,000 — £2,500
Gold Sergeant's at Law ring, English, 16th century, with motto reading 'VIVAT REX ET
LEX', probably relating to Henry VIII.
£3,000 — £4,500
Gold signet ring set with an intaglio cut stone, English, 16th century.
£2,000 — £3,000
Early 17th century gold ring, set with rubies and emeralds.
£1,500 — £2,500
Medieval silver ring brooch of Scottish type.
£1,000 — £1,500

Enamels

The Egyptians discovered and developed the art of enamelling as a natural progression from the process of making glass. Enamel is a form of transparent or opaque glass fused on to or within a metal frame. The metal can be gold, silver, copper or brass and the main techniques used in jewellery are:

1. **Champlevé:** Cups or troughs are cut out of a metal base plate in the required form or motif and molten enamel is poured in. When the enamel has cooled and set it is then rubbed down to a flat, even, surface showing the required design, and then polished to reveal the tops of the "cups" as fine lines of metal. This method is used extensively in Asiatic jewellery.

2. **Cloisonné:** Differs from champlevé in that the design or motif is constructed with thin wires soldered on to a back plate. The molten enamel is then poured into the wire-walled chambers in the same way as before, and the cooled surface is rubbed down and polished. This shows the separating wires in the final design. The Chinese are the greatest craftsmen of cloisonné and many incredibly intricate pieces, including some very large "objets", appear on the market.

3. **Grisaille:** A term referring originally to a fashion of painting in black, grey and white tones which was extended to making enamels in Limoges. It was from this area that the finest medieval painted enamels were produced.

4. **Basse Taille** and **Tour à Guillocher:** Two similar forms of engraving rays and two-dimensional designs into the back plate and building up the enamel in translucent layers to produce a shimmering effect. Used particularly in the late 18th and 19th centuries on lockets and miniature frames, snuffboxes, etc.

5. **Plique-à-Jour:** This is the most difficult and delicate type of enamelling. It was developed in the late 19th century, chiefly in France, and was used extensively in "art nouveau" jewellery. This type of work has no back plate, so the enamel design is clear and translucent, the enamel being held in place by a metal frame. This work is very fragile.

Plate 22

Gold and enamel pendant of Amphrite, set with jewels and pearls, possibly Italian. 4½ins.
(11.5cm) high.
£10,000 — £15,000
Gold, enamelled and jewelled 'Pelican in her Piety'. 4½in. (11.5cm) high.
£7,000 — £10,000
Gold, enamelled and jewelled pendant with the bust of a classical warrior. The frame is
German, c.1600, the centre of a later date. 4⅜ins. (11cm) high.
£10,000 — £15,000
Gold, enamelled and jewelled ship pendant, 4ins. (9.6cm) high.
£10,000 — £15,000

Plate 23

A late 16th century Italian eagle pendant, formed by a large baroque pearl set as the body, surrounded by gold and enamel, with a carbuncle between the feet. 3ins. (7.2cm) high.
£12,000 — £18,000

Plate 24

A fine, late 16th century, South German pendant composed of a large and unusually shaped baroque pearl mounted with diamonds, pearls and enamel to form a merman with an arrow. A beautiful example of the imaginative use of an odd-shaped baroque pearl. 4ins. (9.6cm) high.
£20,000 — £30,000

Plate 25

An important, 16th century, enamelled gold pendant jewel, set with precious stones, made in Augsburg c.1570, close to the manner of Erasmus Hornick. 3⅛in. (7.5cm) high.
£30,000 — £50,000

Plate 26

Late 16th century gold, enamelled and jewelled chain, probably German. 17¾ in. (45cm) long.

£35,000 — £60,000

16th century Italian pendant, the enamelled and jewelled frame set with a fine cameo.

£15,000 — £20,000

Plate 27

(Christie's)

Gold and enamel crucifix in red, blue and white enamel with three pendent pearls,
the Corpus Christie in white enamel.
£4,000 — £6,000

Gold and enamel jewel composed of a crowned eagle in black and white enamel on a
ruby rosette, the mount of blue, red, green and white enamels.
£4,000 — £6,000

Gold and enamelled parrot pendant in red, blue, green and white enamel with
pendent pearls.
£4,500 — £6,000

Gold and enamelled stag pendant with red, blue and mauve enamel, set with
emeralds.
£4,000 — £5,000

(Christie's)

Plate 28

A late 16th century South German necklace and pendant of Diana and a hound, the necklace enamelled in various colours, set with table-cut diamonds, rubies and emeralds, the pendant similar, with the addition of three pearls.

£30,000 — £60,000

(Christie's)

Plate 29

16th century crystal talisman mounted in silver strapwork bands. 1¾ in. (4.5cm) high. The wearing of large pieces of rock crystal was supposed to ward off evil and disease.

£3,500 — £5,000

Late 16th century Italian gold and enamel pendant, the sardonyx cameo of a woman in the Roman style, the reverse (right) a sacrificing priestess, the frame enamelled and set with white pastes. 2¾ in. (7.2cm) high.

£5,000

17th century Spanish emerald and green beryl earrings in girandole form, set in gold.

£900 — £1,200

Late 16th century Spanish, rock crystal and enamel, oval pendant jewel, depicting Adam and Eve and the Tree of Knowledge. 3ins. (7.5cm) high.

£1,500 — £2,500

(Christie's)

Plate 30

Late 17th century, French, enamel riband brooch, c.1670, the enamels finely painted.
2½in. (6cm) diameter.
£8,000 — £12,000
Mid-17th century Hungarian gold and enamel knot of ribbon brooch.
£6,000 — £8,000
Mid-17th century gold, enamelled and jewelled foliage spray brooch, probably English,
2¼in. (5.8cm) high.
£5,000 — £7,000
16th century Spanish gold, enamelled and gem set pendant, 3¼in. (8.5cm) high.
£3,500 — £5,000

(Christie's)

Plate 31

Top to bottom, left to right
17th century Italian gold and enamel earrings, the enamel in pale blue, black
and white with pearls, surmounted by a gold nymph.
£1,500 — £2,000
17th century Spanish gold and enamel rosary, the beads wooden, a double-
spiral green enamel cross supporting the gold Corpus Christie.
£1,800 — £2,200
17th century Italian pendant jewel, the agate cameo set in a frame of rubies,
emeralds and pearls.
£3,750 — £5,750
Late 17th century, French, oval gold and enamel pendant, the stylised flowers
set with rubies, emeralds, diamonds and pearls. This pendant opens to show
St. George and the Dragon in coloured enamels. c.1670.
£5,000 — £6,000

Plate 32

17th century, South German, gold and enamelled diadem, set with pearls, rubies
and emeralds. 4¼ in. (10.8cm) wide.
£6,000 — £8,000

17th century, Hungarian, gold and enamel diadem, set with jewels. Note missing
star left of centre. 8ins. (20.2cm) wide.
£6,000 — £8,000

Plate 33

Late 17th century English necklace set with rubies, table-cut diamonds and emeralds, set in a
scrolled silver and gold mount, the stones foiled.
£6,000 — £10,000

Plate 34

17th century Hungarian emerald and enamelled necklace, the emeralds collet-set and foiled behind, surrounded by enamelled mounts set with pearls and table-cut diamonds, each cluster linked by sections of enamelled chain set with rubies and pearls. (Note the interesting repair in the bottom cluster where a missing table-cut diamond has been replaced by a tear-drop shaped diamond set in a collet, probably from a piece of Spanish jewellery.)

£9,000 — £12,000

(Christie's)

Plate 35

Gold, enamelled and jewelled eagle pendant with pearls pendent from the wingtips. The style of workmanship is coarser than many of the enamelled pieces of the 16th century.

£3,500 — £4,500
£4,500 — £5,500

Plate 36

Italian *verre eglomisé* rock crystal oval pendant with silver-gilt mount.
£1,450 — £1,650
German enamelled double bird brooch, the centre birds of white enamel
with black markings, surrounded by six birds on a green enamel frame.
£1,500 — £1,800
Italian oval pendant of the Annunciation, enamelled in red, green, blue
and white with a black enamel frame.
£1,150 — £1,400
German *verre eglomisé* pendant scent flask in silver-gilt and painted
enamels showing the Annunciation and the Agony in the Garden.
£1,500 — £2,000+

(S.J. Phillips)

Plate 37

Left to right, top to bottom
Enamel cross with Corpus Christie and skull, mounted with gold, possibly Germany.
£1,000 — £1,200
Spanish gold and enamel oval religious pendant with stylised bow top.
£1,000 — £1,200
German garnet and gold cross, the garnets inlaid with enamelled symbols depicting scenes
from 'the Betrayal and Crucifixion of Christ'. The loops from each arm and the base of the
cross were probably to suspend pearls.
£1,000 — £1,400
North European stone cameo set in an enamelled frame with rubies and diamonds, c.1650.
Cameo now in V & A Jewellery display
Spanish pendant, the miniature set in a frame of filigree gold with a stylised floral crown.
£750 — £950
English enamelled gold cross set with rubies, suspended from a bow.
£3,000 — £4,000
English, stylised cross, enamelled and set with foiled rubies.
£1,000 — £1,500

(Christie's)

Plate 38

A pair of 16th century Italian earrings in the form of ships, gold with white enamel and pendent pearls.
£3,000 — £4,000

A 17th century French 'memento mori' in the form of a white enamelled skull which opens to show an altar with a crucifix and a skeleton below.
£3,500 — £4,000

A 16th century Venetian ship pendant, blue, green and white enamel with seed pearls in gold.
£3,000 — £3,500

18th century South German seal formed of a baroque pearl with parcel-gilt figures.
£1,700 — £2,500

Louis XV blackamoor seal in sardonyx and gold, c.1730. (There was a considerable interest in blackamoors as slaves and servants at this period, although to find them in jewellery form is not common.)
£1,500 — £1,800

19th century Spanish gold and enamel doll pendant, c.1830.
£900 — £1,200

George III vinaigrette in the form of a basket in agate and gold, late 18th century.
£2,000 — £2,500

Plate 39

Left to right, top to bottom

16th century Spanish gold and enamel pendant of a centaur, enamelled in blue and white, his
body set with an emerald. 2¾ in. (7cm) high.

£3,000 — £3,500

Late 17th century Flemish gold and enamel fob seal, two putti at the altar of love, their
wings of gold, their bodies of blue and white enamel, the cornelian intaglio on the base of a
seated Roman. 1¼ in. (3.2cm) high.

£2,300 — £2,700

A rare mid-16th century pendant, the gold roundel of David with the head of Goliath.
Italian or French. 3¾ in. (9.5cm) high.

£4,000 — £4,500

A late 16th century Spanish pendant jewel of the crucifixion, 2¼ in. (5.8cm) high.

£4,000 — £4,500

A large baroque pearl mounted as the torso of a merman, gold and enamelled. 3¾ ins.
(9.5cm) high.

£3,000 — £3,500

18th century German table seal, set with baroque pearls, diamonds, coloured enamels, the
intaglio of the base sardonyx matrix engraved with Hercules strangling a viper. 2½ ins.
(6.5cm) high.

£3.200 — £3,750

Plate 40

Left to right, top to bottom

A pair of 17th century Spanish earrings, the brown-foiled topazes set in silver.
£1,100 — £1,500

18th century, brown-foiled topaz, girandole brooch, set in silver.
£1,000 — £1,500

17th century oval brooch pavé set with chrysoberyls in gold. This type of jewellery of the 17th and 18th centuries is often referred to as 'chrysolite jewellery', and was particularly popular in Spain and Portugal since chryso-beryls were mined in Brazil.
£3,000 — £3,500

17th century Spanish enamel brooch in a gold and emerald frame.
£2,000 — £2,500

17th century Stuart oval memorial ribbon slide, formed of hair surmounted with two putti supporting a skull, under a section of faceted crystal, mounted in gold, dated 4 June 1696.
£1,900 — £2,200

Early 18th century octagonal memorial ribbon slide, the hair-work decorated with gold thread under crystal.
£1,500 — £2,000

18th century oval memorial ribbon slide of crystal and gold, dated 1714. On either side, it is just possible to see the shallow gold loops where the slide was threaded on a ribbon and worn round the neck, or possibly the wrist.
£500 — £800

17th century black and white enamel, garnet and emerald pendant of open-work design, the back enamelled.
£500 — £800

(Cameo Corner)

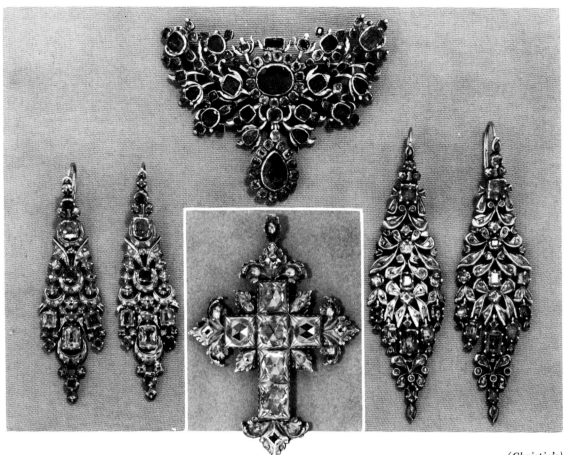

Plate 42

17th century Spanish emerald and green beryl brooch, the stones foiled and set in gold.
£2,500 — £3,000
18th century Spanish emerald and green beryl earrings with small rose-cut diamonds.
£1,800 — £2,200
18th century Spanish emerald, green beryl and rose diamond earrings. These long drop
earrings are typical of 17th and 18th century Spanish and Portuguese designs.
£1,800 — £2,200
Late 17th century French diamond and enamel cross, set with large rose diamonds in silver,
the reverse painted in enamels with peonies on a white ground, the centre compartment
hinged.
£10,000

Plate 41 *(see opposite)*

Left to right, top to bottom
Spanish crowned gold pendant set with diamonds, rubies and emeralds with a centre enamel plaque,
period 1680-1720. *£3,000 — £3,500*
Spanish gold open-work pendant set with diamonds with an 'Infant Jesus' centre, c.1690.
£2,000 — £2,500
Sentimental brooch mounted with rose-cut diamonds in a silver setting, depicting a Cupid firing
an arrow at a heart, c.1740. *£2,750 — £3,500*
Ruby, diamond and centre garnet 'star' pendant in gold and silver, c.1700.
£3,500 — £4,000
Filigree gold drop pendant with black and white enamel set with small drilled pearls, probably
French, c.1680. *£300 — £400*
45

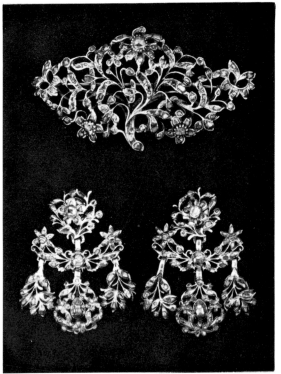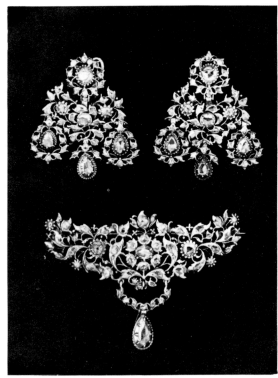

(Christie's)

Plate 43

18th century, rose diamond set, stomacher brooch and earrings *en suite,* probably Spanish. Note the flat stylised design of the brooch, pinned centrally on the bodice, hence the term 'stomacher'.

£3,000 — £4,000

Late 17th century, Spanish, rose diamond brooch and earrings *en suite,* of open floral design with pendent drops. The design of the brooch suggests that pendent drops are missing from either side of the central motif.

£3,000 — £4,000

Plate 44

Mid-18th century suite of brooch and earrings in a floral pattern, rose diamonds set in silver, probably French, c.1730. The delicate floral setting shows the minimum use of silver in the setting of the small rose diamonds, and the suite is complete with original fittings.

£4,000 — £6,000

Plate 45

A mid-18th century Spanish gold and rose diamond open-work necklace. This piece would probably have been sewn on to a ribbon and tied at the back of the neck.

£4,000 — £6,000

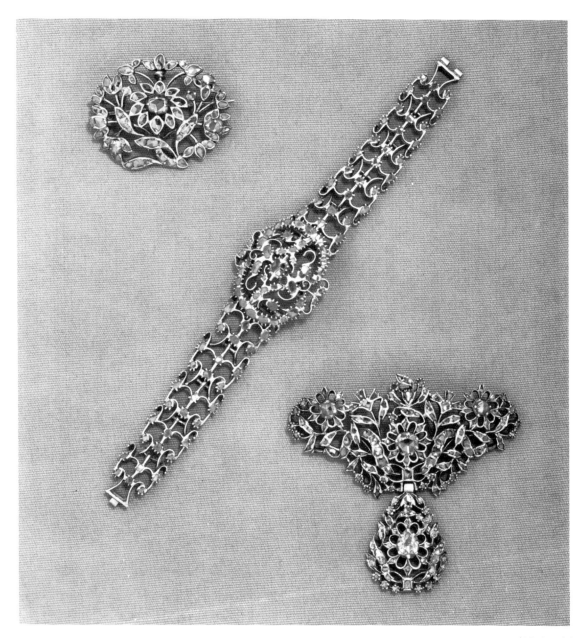

Plate 46

18th century, Spanish, rose diamond, flower cluster brooch set in silver.
£1,000 — £1,500
18th century, Portuguese, rose diamond bracelet, the open-link scroll design in silver.
£2,500 — £4,000 depending on foiling
18th century, Spanish or Portuguese, rose diamond floral pendant with a floral cluster drop, set in silver. The side drops are missing, the bars to take them being clearly visible.
£2,000 — £4,000

Plate 47

18th century French diamond bow brooch, set in silver.
£5,000 — £8,000
A pair of 18th century Spanish emerald and green beryl earrings, set in
gold. Note the tops of the original earring fittings showing. The emeralds
are pale in colour and foiled.
£2,000 — £3,500

Plate 48

Left to right, top to bottom
18th century Spanish ring, the pearl and rose diamond mount set with a classical style cameo.
£600 — £700
17th century Spanish diamond cluster ring, set in gold with diamonds, typically Spanish and Portuguese. French and English work of the same date will normally be mounted either in silver throughout, or the stones set in silver and back with gold for strength. This ring may have started life as a button.
£1,750 — £2,000
17th century Spanish marquise-shaped ring, of gold open-work design set with emeralds.
£1,500 — £1,750
18th century ruby and diamond heart-shaped ring.
£900 — £1,300
18th century ruby and diamond crowned double heart ring.
£2,000 — £2,500
18th century, French, ruby and diamond, crowned double heart ring.
£1,200 — £1,600
18th century, Spanish, emerald and rose diamond circular cluster ring, all the stones foiled and set in gold.
£1,500 — £2,000
18th century, French, emerald and diamond cluster ring with gem-set shoulders.
£1,750 — £2,200
18th century, English, ruby and diamond ring, the centre ruby surrounded by table-cut diamonds. (The ruby is weak in colour and this affects the price.)
£1,250 — £1,700

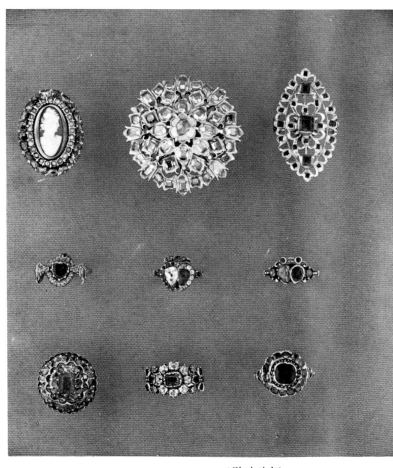

(Christie's)

Plate 49
18th century Spanish necklace with large pendant attached, emeralds and rose diamonds set
in gold.
£8,000 — £12,000

Plate 50 *(see opposite)*

Suite of corsage ornament and cross pendant with earrings. Metal gilt and glass, probably south
European, c.1750. *£600 — £750*
Pair very large jacinth (hessonite garnet) and gold drop earrings, Spanish or Portuguese, c.1750.
£1,500 — £2,000

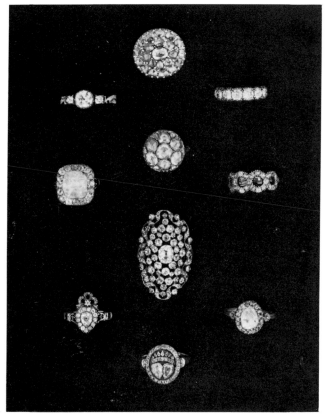

(Christie's)

Plate 51

Top to bottom, left to right
Spanish, circular, pavé set, rose diamond cluster ring.
£1,500 — £2,000
English memorial ring, the cushion-cut diamonds set in a white enamelled scrolled hoop.
£1,500 — £2,000
Graduated diamond seven stone half-hoop ring.
£1,200 — £1,600
English rose diamond seven stone circular cluster ring.
£1,750 — £2,200
English diamond cluster ring, the cushion-cut stone centre diamond surrounded by
smaller cushion-cut stones.
£3,000 — £5,000
French diamond half-hoop ring, formed of linked open circles set with diamonds.
£1,600 — £2,000
Large, French, open-work oval diamond ring with a diamond set scrolled border.
£1,900 — £2,400
English diamond crowned heart ring.
£1,750 — £2,200
English oval rose diamond cluster ring with engraved back.
£2,000 — £3,000
English diamond crowned double heart ring, on enamel background with a circular diamond
border.
£2,000 — £3,000

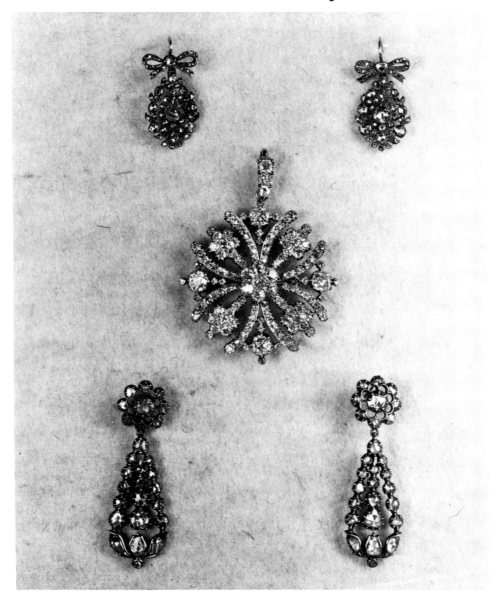

(Christie's)

Plate 52

Top to bottom
Mid-18th century rose diamond drop earrings of open-work design with ribbon
bow tops, set in silver, English, c.1760.
£1,500 — £1,750
Late 18th century stylised Maltese cross set with old brilliant-cut diamonds,
English, c.1790.
£6,000+
A pair of late 18th century rose diamond drop earrings, set in silver, c.1790.
£1,750 — £2,250

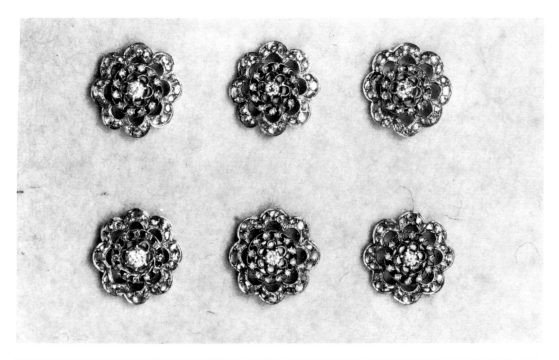

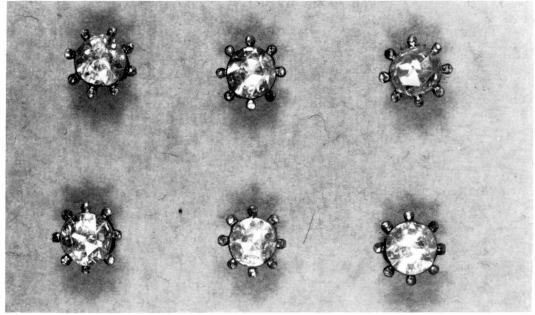

Plate 53

A set of six 18th century, English, rose diamond buttons in the form of stylised
flowers. This type of work is more often seen in paste.
£6,000
A set of six 18th century, Continental, diamond buttons, each large circular rose
diamond surrounded by eight smaller ones.
£10,000 — £20,000

56

Plate 54

Late 18th century necklace of rose diamonds surrounded by small cushion-cut diamonds forming graduated circular and lozenge shaped clusters, set in silver. The double snaps of the necklace can be fitted to a central brooch or pendant (not shown), so that the necklace is in fact upside down.
£12,000+
Early 19th century Maltese cross with fleur-de-lys at the intersections, cushion-cut diamond set in silver and backed with gold.
£6,000+

Cut Steel

Cut steel was popular as a form of jewellery from the middle of the 18th century in England and was made in Birmingham where it was an important part of the jewellery industry. A base metal mount, usually brass, was pierced with small holes very close together in the pattern required. Round steel heads, but some crescent or star shaped, were rose-cut and polished and then pavé set in the pierced holes. Each piece of steel was held in place by steel rivets which fitted into the holes in the base plate. This was a long and skilful process which was superseded during the Industrial Revolution in the 19th century by die-stamped "cut steel".

Since cut steel will rust if it gets damp or wet, and is difficult to repolish or clean, it was often discarded.

General Price Guide: Individual piece £150 — £300.

(E. Ashley Cooper)

Plate 55

A fine 18th century cut steel necklace, pavé set, c.1780.
£300 — £350

Plate 56

Left to right,
top to bottom
Scroll and arrow brooch.
Twelve petalled flower
brooch.
Long drop pendant
(probably made from an
earring).
Butterfly brooch.
Target brooch.
Anchor and star brooch.
Horseshoe ribbon slide or
buckle.
Shoe buckle in open-work
design.
Bird in flight.
Generally up to £150
Necklace formed in inter-
linking rosettes with three
pendants.
£300 — £350

(Cameo Corner)

Plate 57

Left to right, top to bottom
Late 18th century topaz set bow with pendant drop, the topazes foiled and set in silver, c.1770.
£750 — £850
Mid-18th cetnury, open-work floral drop brooch, the amethysts table-cut, and rose-cut diamonds
set and backed with silver, probably French.
£2,000 — £2,500
Mid-18th century, flat-cut garnet double cluster brooch, pavé set, in silver. c.1760.
£650 — £850
Late 18th century, marquise-shaped blue enamel and diamond brooch, set with a large 18th century
cushion-cut diamond in silver, the whole brooch backed with gold, c.1790.
£3,000 — £3,500
Early 18th century cross pendent from a bow, set with table-cut and rose-cut diamonds in gold,
Spanish or Portuguese.
£3,000 — £4,000
Georgian, emerald and diamond, circular cluster brooch, the emerald open-set, the diamonds in
a close setting in silver, c.1780.
£20,000+
18th century, floral open-work Catherine wheel brooch, the centre of black enamel set with rubies
and diamonds, the frame of rubies, emeralds and diamonds, in silver and backed with gold, c.1770.
£1,750 — £2,100
Early 18th century ruby and rose diamond cross, set and back with silver and gold.
£2,000 — £2,500
18th century rose diamond cluster necklace, set and backed with silver, c.1770.

£12,000+

(S.J. Phillips)

(Christie's)

Plate 58

18th century pavé set diamond *St. Esprit,* c.1780. *St. Esprits* were usually made in Flanders, popular throughout the late 18th and first half of the 19th centuries, frequently seen with large sprays of foliage, symbolising the Dove of Peace bearing an olive branch.
£6,000+

Late 18th century diamond choker formed of graduated linked sections (four extra sections also shown), c.1800. A beautiful and rare piece of jewellery.
£10,000+

Diamonds

Diamonds are pure carbon crystals and are the hardest substance known to man. The main colour is white, although as can be seen from the frontispiece, diamonds occur in a variety of fancy colours, thus enabling the jeweller to produce fascinating and exciting designs. They are the most common of the four main precious stones, the other three being ruby, emerald and sapphire.

Traditionally, diamond is the emblem of love and fearlessness. The finest diamonds are graded as "finest white" and any diamond that is not white, or is an off-shade of white, is referred to as "coloured" or "fancy", with the appropriate colour. Blue-white is a term used to denote a diamond with a distinct bluish tinge due to natural fluorescence. Another term often used is "of the first water"; this is not a gemmological term and means nothing. Diamond has a natural brilliance which has captivated man over the centuries, and the stone has been sought after from early times.

The earliest mining of diamonds was in India, and historically is thought to have dated from around 500 BC. The most important mining area was Golconda. Borneo and Indonesia have also produced stones since the Dark Ages, and these three places were the major sources of world supply until the discovery of diamonds in Brazil in the early 18th century. The impetus that this discovery gave to the diamond trade meant that large quantities of jewellery were produced in Europe in the 18th and 19th centuries. It was not until the discovery of diamonds in Australia in the middle of the 19th century, and far more important, the discoveries in South Africa around the turn of the century, that diamonds began to fall within the price range of ordinary people. Since then, diamonds have been found in large quantities in Africa — in Angola, S.W. Africa, Zaire, Sierra Leone and so on — and more recently in Russia. Only a minority of all stones mined throughout the world are of gem quality and the great bulk are used in industry for grinding and cutting. Diamonds are found in "pipes" in a substance known as blue ground, or in alluvial deposits such as the beds of streams. In some cases they are mined from the sea where the sand that contains them is sucked up from the sea-bed and filtered.

The cutting of diamonds has developed in order to show the stones at their best, the "brilliant" cut being the most effective. Diamonds have been cut in many different ways but their brilliance is sometimes sacrificed in order to produce a different shape of stone, such as baguette or trap-cut. See pages 342 and 343.

Technicalities: Chemical composition: carbon. Crystal structure: cubic, forming octahedra, dodecahedra, 24- and even 48-sided crystals. Hardness: 10. S.G.: 3.52. R.I.: 2.42. Diamonds are basically classified in terms of their worth under the headings of clarity and colour. Clarity means exactly what it says. A flawless stone is a stone that shows no inclusions at all under a $10\times$ magnification jeweller's glass. Diamonds are graded from "flawless" to "heavily spotted", i.e. including spots of carbon, flaws and discoloration. Colour is graded from "finest white" to "cape". We have referred to hardness in stones. The hardness of stones is mentioned throughout the book, each natural crystal and aggregate having its own hardness which is a means of identification. Synthetic gem diamonds are still too expensive to produce to take the place of natural stones. However, they have been imitated in jewellery by white zircons, sapphires, crystals and pastes, all of which should be easily identified by the experienced eye. Synthetically-made imitations such as strontium titanate (fabulite), YAG (cirolite, diamonair or diagem), synthetic rutile and synthetic white spinels and sapphires may fool members of the public who are not used to handling them, but they should not fool the expert!

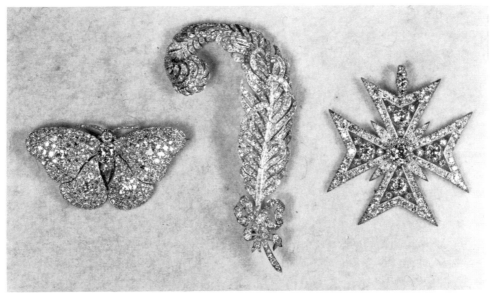

Plate 59

Pavé set diamond butterfly, English, c.1770.
£5,000 — £6,500
Diamond ostrich plume brooch with diamond set bow, c.1867 by O. Massim.
£3,500 — £4,500
Diamond set Maltese cross, English, c.1780.
£3,000 — £4,000
A fine pair of diamond ostrich feather brooches with articulated sections, allowing a 'tremblant' effect. They were probably worn in a high towered hair style, c.1780.
£8,000 the pair

Plate 59 includes some examples of the best designs and workmanship of the late 18th century.

Plate 60

18th century diamond necklace in the form of a chain, set in silver. The necklace will divide to form two bracelets.
£10,000 — £15,000

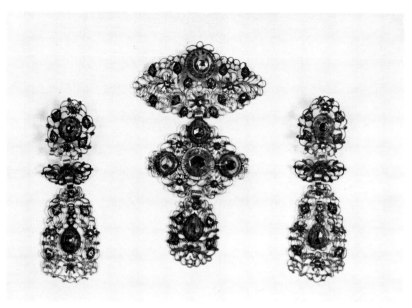

(Cameo Corner)

Plate 61

An early 18th century gold filigree brooch with earrings *en suite,* set with rose
diamonds, probably Northern French, c.1700.
£1,500 — £2,000

Plate 62 *(see opposite)*

Left to right, top to bottom
Georgian diamond spray brooch set in silver and gold, c.1820.
£20,000+
Victorian diamond spray brooch, the flowerhead 'en tremblant' and set with a ruby, c.1845.
£10,000 — £15,000
Reproduction diamond spray brooch, set with 'old cut' diamonds in silver and gold, using the
same methods of crafsmanship as the originals.
£10,000 — £15,000
Georgian diamond flower spray brooch, 'en tremblant' and pavé set, c.1800.
£10,000 — £15,000
Small Georgian rose diamond flower brooch, closed back, c.1800.
£1,000 — £1,200
Fine long Georgian gold guard chain, the hand clasp set with a turquoise. This is a particularly
fine example of this type of chain, much sought after and always fashionable. The originals were
light in weight and either finely granulated or plain-linked. Modern reproductions are heavy and
coarse and should be about one-third of the price. Georgian gold clasps were often made in the
form of single or clasped hands and were finely tooled.
£2,750 — £3,250

(Wartski)

(Christie's)

Plate 63

An 18th century diamond suite of necklace and earrings in girandole form, the linked ribbon loops and pendant sections set with rose and cushion-cut diamonds. An elaborate and formal suite with a large weight of set stones.
£40,000

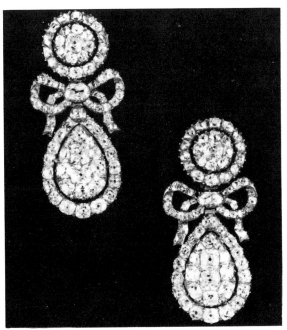 

(Sotheby's)

Plate 64

A fine pair of 18th century diamond drop earrings, the stones pavé set in a closed setting.
c.1780.
£7,000 — £9,000
A fine pair of late 18th century diamond pendant earrings with a lace-like bow in the centre.
(The top clusters of the earrings have been modified at a later date.)
£8,000 — £10,000

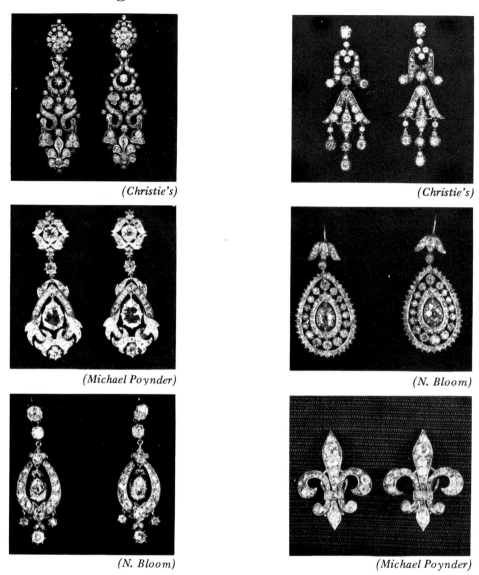

Plate 65

Left to right, top to bottom
A pair of Georgian earrings set with brilliant and rose diamonds.
£2,500 — £3,000
A pair of Victorian diamond drop earrings with three pendent drops, set in silver and gold.
£1,800 — £2,200
A pair of Victorian diamond drop earrings, the centre large diamond free-swinging in a
scrolled frame, mounted in silver and gold, c.1875.
£5,000+
A pair of Georgian diamond pear-shaped drop earrings in a closed back setting, c.1800.
£2,500 — £3,500
A pair of Victorian diamond drop earrings with pendent drops, c.1860.
£2,500 — £3,500
A pair of Victorian diamond fleur-de-lys earclips, c.1840.
£1,500 — £2,000

Plate 66

Early 18th century diamond suite of necklace, earrings and brooch, set in silver.
Reputedly this suite was offered as ransom by Empress Catherine of Russia after
the capture of Peter the Great at the Battle of Rusen in 1711.
£150,000 — £250,000

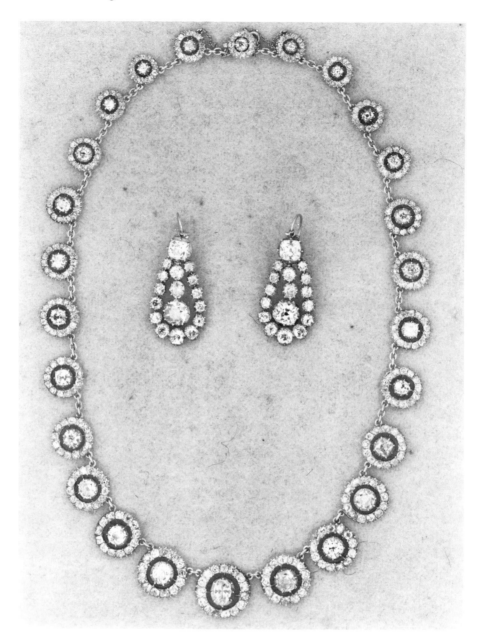

(Christie's)

Plate 67

A late 18th century diamond necklace formed of twenty-five graduated clusters set with cushion-cut diamonds, English, c.1780. This is the type of necklace that is bought at auction 'for break', since twenty-five diamond cluster rings could certainly sell for more than the price of the whole necklace.
£50,000 — £75,000
A fine pair of Georgian diamond drop earrings, the cushion-cut diamonds foiled and backed with gold, English, c.1780.
£5,000 — £6,000

(Christie's)

Plate 68

Georgian diamond collet necklace with five graduated sapphire and diamond cluster pendants attached, the necklace c.1830, the clusters, c.1870. This was presumably 'made up' at some time, and would probably be 'broken up' again today to make either earrings or rings, depending on how the individual sapphires matched for colour.

£100,000 — £200,000

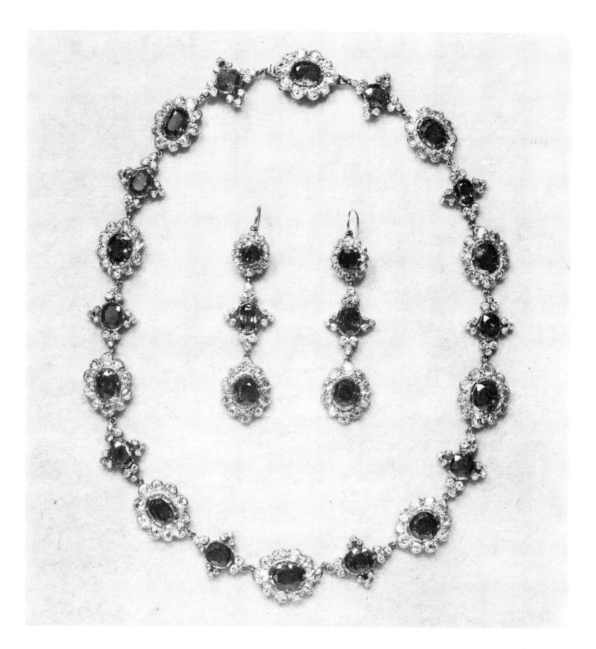

Plate 69

19th century ruby and diamond suite of earrings and necklace, the rubies foiled in a closed setting, c.1825. The earrings are made from sections of the necklace, as the style is identical rather than being 'en suite'.
£35,000 — £50,000

Plate 70

A magnificent late 18th century diamond tiara with a detachable ostrich plume of diamonds set in silver and gold. The ostrich plume may also be worn separately as an aigrette, brooch, or corsage ornament. English, c.1800. Formerly in the collection of the 7th Duke of Newcastle. This tiara epitomises the Napoleonic Era. So many portraits and cartoons of the period depict women wearing jewels and plumes like this, but this example must surely be one of the finest for its grandeur and 'style'.

£250,000

Diamond Jewellery, 1760-1800

(S.J. Phillips)

Plate 71

Left to right, top to bottom

Six-petalled flower brooch set with rose-cut diamonds, each petal linked by a diamond collet.

£2,000 — £3,000

Marquise-shaped rose diamond cluster ring, the stones pavé set.

£1,800 — £2,500

A pair of diamond drop earrings, cushion cut diamonds set in a cut-down collet setting, with rare pendeloque-cut diamond drops.

£14,000 — £18,000

Rose diamond set wheatsheaf brooch, backed with gold, c.1770.

£2,000

Stylised four-lobed target brooch, the open-work design set with cushion-cut and rose-cut diamonds, c.1780.

£1,750 — £2,250

Six-petalled diamond flower brooch, the cushion-cut diamonds set in silver, the mount curved to give the brooch 'shape'.

£3,000 — £4,000

Round diamond cluster ring, set with cushion-cut diamonds.

£2,000 — £2,500

A pair of large diamond drop earrings, the centre diamond sections unusually backed with glass.

£10,000 — £12,000

Pavé set diamond St. Esprit, set with rose diamonds in silver, c.1780.

£1,200 — £1,500

A pair of diamond leaf spray brooches, set with cushion-cut diamonds, c.1760.

£1,400 — £1,700

Rubies

Rubies are probably the rarest of the four main precious stones and are red in colour. They belong to the gem species called Corundum which has only one other group, sapphire. They occur in mines and alluvial deposits in conjunction with various semi-precious stones.

Rubies have always had superstition attached to them because they are the colour of blood, and in the Far East where they are mainly found they are considered to enhance the wearer's divinity and protect him against force and illness. Unlike most gemstones, rubies do not occur in large sizes and stones of the finest colour and clarity seldom weigh more than a few carats. A 5ct. stone of top quality is considered of importance, and over 10cts. a great rarity.

The finest stones come from the mines in the Mogok area of Burma where they have been mined for centuries. These stones are of a beautiful bright red, often referred to as "pigeon's blood" red. Burma is now an independent country and its frontiers have virtually been closed to foreigners. Little information is available as to current production, but it is rumoured that mining still continues and that the Burmese economy is backed by stones rather than gold. Although Thailand is next door to Burma, the rubies of that country are not of the same colour and quality, tending to be darker, often with a brownish tinge, and commonly referred to as Siam rubies, to differentiate quality. Rubies are found all over the Indian sub-continent, and Sri Lanka (Ceylon) in particular produces a large quantity from the Ratnapura area. However, they tend to be pale and pinkish, and are not used a great deal in Western jewellery. Although these are the main sources, in recent years reports have appeared of gem quality rubies being found in Africa, but not of any significant size.

The most usual cut is a combination of a brilliant-cut crown and a step-cut pavilion, and most stones are "native-cut", i.e. faceted and polished by the miners at source. This is easily discernible, even to the inexperienced eye as the facets are not uniform, and the shape of the cut stones by no means symmetrical, having been cut to give maximum weight and to show their best colour. Some rubies (and sapphires), because of their crystal formation, when cut *en cabochon* show a property known as asterism. This is a whitish, six- (and sometimes twelve-) rayed star best viewed under a direct light. These stones are seldom the finer reds (or blues) and are usually translucent to opaque and paler in colour. They are known as star rubies or sapphires, and are particularly popular with Asiatics and Americans (see in colour in Plate 196).

Technicalities: Chemical composition: aluminium oxide (Al_2O_3). Crystal structure: trigonal, forming hexagonal crystals. Hardness: 9. S.G.: 3.99. R.I.: 1.76-1.77. Ruby is coloured by chromium, and the darker colour and brownish tint in Siam stones is due to traces of iron. Synthetic rubies are made in laboratories, usually by the Verneuil process, but they are distinguishable to an expert since they are too perfect, the colour too good, and they will show inclusions of minute gas bubbles rather than any of the small natural inclusions normally found in natural stones. Synthetic star-stones are also made by the Verneuil process, but their body-colour is usually much stronger than in natural star-stones, and the rays of the star much sharper. A particular inclusion in natural stones is known as "silk", and through a jeweller's glass it looks like a very fine layer of white silk strands.

"Balas ruby" is a misnomer applied to red spinel, particularly in medieval times, when, gemmologically, stones were not always distinguishable one from another. Spinels are often doubled with glass or crystal in order to pass them off as rubies.

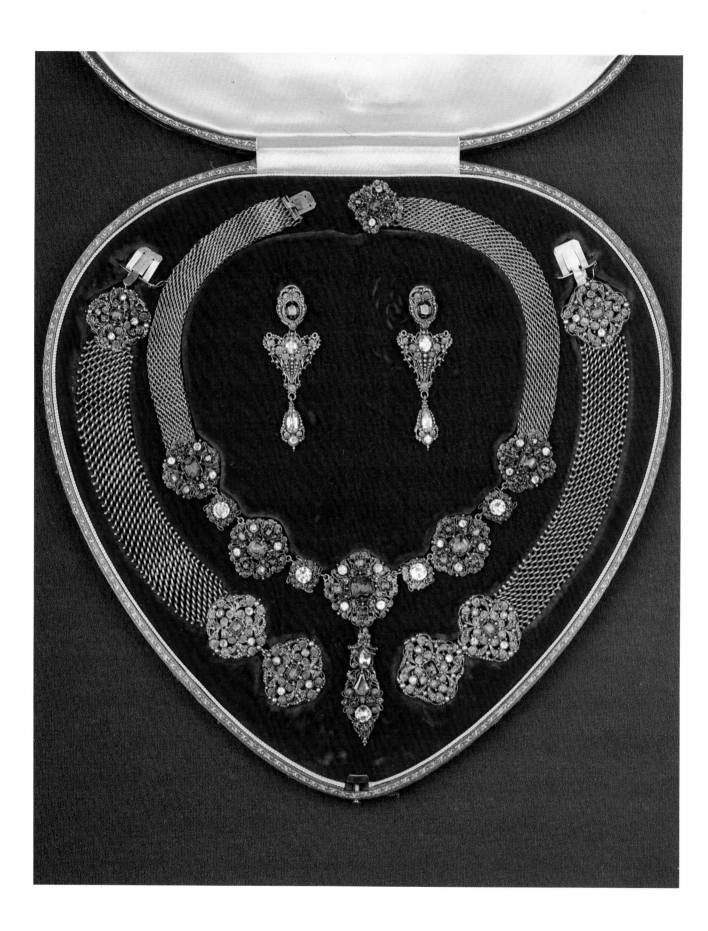

Emeralds

Emeralds are green in colour. They belong to a gem species called Beryl, which also includes aquamarine (pale greenish-blue), golden beryl (yellow) and morganite (pink). Emeralds are usually found on their own whereas the other three are often mined together.

There is a certain superstition attached to emeralds because of their colour, and they are still thought to be unlucky. Although they are hard stones, they have a fracture property and nearly always show inclusions and marks to the naked eye. A "clean" emerald should be treated with suspicion as it might well be a synthetic.

They have been mined since archaic times, originally in Egypt, although these stones were of poor quality. The most famous and lasting source is in South America (Colombia) and the original abundant supply of fine stones came to Europe for the first time after the Spanish Conquest. The main Colombian mines are called Muzo, Chivor and Cosquez, and still supply top quality stones. A small number of stones are mined in Brazil, but they are generally of poor quality. Other known sources still in use today are Russia (Ural Mts.) mined from 1830 onwards, Australia, 1890 onwards, and South Africa, 1920 onwards. India and Pakistan produced emeralds in ancient times, but the mines were only reopened in the 1940s. Zimbabwe (Rhodesia), Tanzania, Zambia and Zaire have produced emeralds during the last few years, and stones from the Sandawana mine in Zimbabwe (Rhodesia) can be of excellent quality. Other minor sources are Norway, USA (S. Carolina) and Mozambique.

The finer stones are normally step-cut, also known as emerald-cut, as this shows their natural colour to best advantage. Small stones are brilliant-cut and are used extensively with other small stones in jewellery. Lesser quality stones may be cut "en cabochon" or as beads. Occasionally, emeralds are cut as cameos or intaglios, but this is difficult due to the fracture properties already mentioned.

Technicalities: Chemical composition: beryllium aluminium silicate ($Be_3Al_2(SiO_3)_6$). Crystal structure: hexagonal, forming hexagonal prisms. Hardness: 7¾. S.G.: 2.69-2.75. R.I.: 1.56-1.59. Synthetics are laboratory-made in the USA (some are marketed as Chatham emeralds) and are often used in jewellery. Clear beryl and quartz doublets with a green gelatine "sandwich" are also used but are easily discernible with a jeweller's glass. Emeralds generally show red through the Chelsea Colour Filter which may be used as a rough guide to help identification.

Stop Press — *Elizabeth Ashley Cooper tried to visit the Colombian mines in June 1976 but they were firmly closed with troops and machine guns attendant!*

Plate 72 *(see opposite)*

Emerald and diamond suite in granulated gold setting, c.1820.

(S.J. Phillips)

(S.J. Phillips)

Plate 73

A Georgian flat-cut garnet composite suite of necklace, brooch, two pendants and earrings, set and backed with gold, c.1770-1820. All original except the left-hand cross pendant which repeats sections of the necklace and has a modern pendant loop — an 'original' reproduction. Reproduction garnet suites are made today but the workmanship is coarser, the setting thicker and therefore a lot heavier.

£3,000+

Plate 74

A fine Georgian aquamarine and filigree gold suite of necklace and earrings, the aquamarines
foiled and backed with gold, set in a filigree gold mount of *cannetille* work, English, c.1830.
£7,000 — £10,000

Sapphires

Sapphires belong to the Corundum family. They are best known as blue, but in fact occur in just about every colour possible, including a deep pink when they resemble rubies (the other member of the Corundum family).

Blue sapphires are particularly popular in the Western world, as they go so well with the natural colouring of the women of the Northern races who have blue or grey eyes and pale skins. Amongst the peoples of the Middle and Far East the sapphire has a peculiar superstition attached to it, whereby it is supposed either to bring the wearer great luck and fortune, or, great misfortune; but it is not until the owner has worn the actual stone that he or she will know which way fortune will swing. This superstition is only attached to the colour blue, and to blue sapphires, which is why one seldom sees blue sapphires or blue enamel in "native jewellery". Stones of the finest quality occur in larger sizes than either rubies or emeralds and superb stones in excess of 50cts. appear on the market.

Sapphires are found in different parts of the world and vary enormously in quality and colour. The finest ones are considered to come from Burma and Kashmir. The Burma stones are a deep royal blue without any hint of mauve, and have a great deal of "life" and brilliance. Kashmir stones are particularly fine and have their own colour range which is hard to describe: it is a royal blue, but with a very slight milky appearance due to minute inclusions of "silk" (already mentioned in connection with rubies). They are considered by some experts to be even finer than the best Burmese stones. The mines in Kashmir are at over 14,000 feet above sea-level, and for much of the year are inaccessible due to the extremes of climate. Thailand is a major source of sapphires, but they tend to be dark and a duller blue and therefore are not nearly as costly. Sri Lanka produces probably the greatest amount of gem quality sapphires in the world, from the Ratnapura area. The characteristic colour here is known as "cornflower" blue, and they can be beautiful stones of great brilliance and size. Sri Lanka is also the main producer of the "fancy-coloured" sapphires: white, yellow, purple, green, pink and a very rare colour — peachy orange — known as Padparascha, which means lotus blossom. It is most unusual to find a really good blue stone showing the property of asterism. Star sapphires are translucent and have a base-colour of greyish-blue. Australia produces a large quantity of blue stones, but they tend to be inky, over-dark and usually have a greenish tinge. They are not considered to compare in quality with the Asiatic stones. The only other major source is Montana, USA, and these are easily recognisable for their intense steely blue. They seldom occur in large sizes, but are used in art nouveau and 20th century jewellery.

The usual cuts apply to sapphires — step-cut, brilliant-cut, mixed-cut, *cabochon* (the only cut used for star stones), and beads. Native-cut sapphires are common, even in highly sophisticated jewellery produced by some of the great jewellery houses, since to re-cut the stone in modern terms would not necessarily enhance its colour and it would certainly lose weight. Native cutters have an instinctive eye and centuries of inherited experience in faceting stones. When cutting a parti-coloured stone, they have the ability to facet it in such a way as to show the greatest amount of colour throughout the stone. This is done by cutting it with the strongest colour at the base, so that the stone appears to have a uniform colour when viewed through the table, whereas if viewed from the side, it might be almost clear except for a small concentration of colour near the pavilion. These parti-coloured stones are described as having "windows", which means that when tilted a clear view through a colourless part of the stone becomes visible. Naturally this detracts from the value of the stone.

Technicalities: Chemical composition: aluminium oxide (Al_2O_3). Crystal structure: trigonal, forming bi-pyramids. Hardness: 9. S.G.: 3.99. R.I.: 1.76-1.77. Synthetic sapphires are made in laboratories by the Verneuil process, as are star sapphires. When viewed through the jeweller's glass or microscope, they normally show curved colour bands as opposed to straight bands in natural stones, and minute gas bubbles may also be visible. Synthetic white sapphires are sometimes used to imitate diamonds.

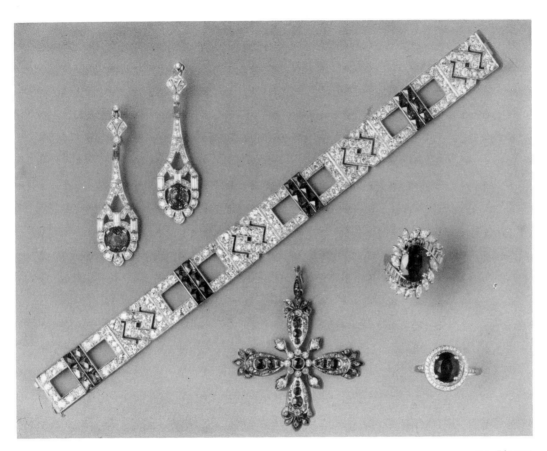

(N. Bloom)

Plate 75

Pair platinum mounted diamond and baguette diamond earrings set with Ceylon sapphires, c.1920.
£6,000 — £8,000
Platinum mounted diamond bracelet set with 4 twin-rows of French-cut Ceylon sapphires, c.1930.
£10,000 — £15,000
Edwardian silver and gold-mounted cross pendant set with diamonds and sapphires, c.1900.
£1,800 — £2,200
Ring with marquise and baguette diamond swirl mount set with a Burma sapphire estimated 6cts., c.1950.
£25,000
Ring set Burma sapphire estimated 4cts. twin-row diamond surround, c.1910.
£6,000 — £10,000

Plate 76 *(see opposite)*

Left to right, top to bottom
Mid-Victorian, ruby and diamond star brooch, set in silver and gold, c.1860.
£6,000 — £8,000
Mid-Victorian, amethyst and diamond, oval cluster brooch, set in silver and gold, c.1860.
£5,000 — £6,000
Early Victorian, carved cabochon garnet, diamond and pearl-shaped cluster brooch which also
forms the centre and clasp of a bracelet, c.1840.
£4,000 — £5,000
Early Victorian, emerald and diamond, shaped cluster brooch, set in silver and gold, c.1850.
£7,000+
Early Victorian, sapphire and diamond, peacock-feather brooch set in silver and gold, c.1840.
£6,000 — £7,500
Cabochon emerald, ruby, sapphire and diamond open-work floral brooch in early 19th century
style, mounted in silver and gold.
£4,500 — £6,000
Late Georgian, fine pink topaz and diamond, rectangular cluster brooch, set in silver and gold,
open-backed, c.1830.
£6,000 — £7,000

(S.J. Phillips)

Plate 77

A pair of large early 19th century
diamond oak-sprays, set with
cushion-cut diamonds in silver and
gold, English, c.1810. A lovely
pair of spray brooches, unusual in
jewellery, a design illustrating
English patriotism during the
Napoleonic Wars and the Regency
period.
£25,000 — £40,000

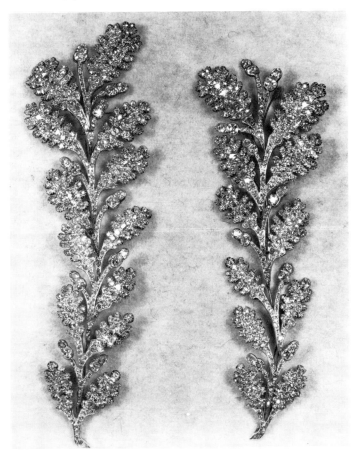

(Christie's)

(Tessiers)

Plate 78

Georgian pavé-set diamond six-petalled flower, set in silver with closed back, c.1790.
£7,000+
Early Victorian diamond flower spray brooch with 'tremblant' flower head, mounted in
silver and gold, c.1840.
£7,000+
Georgian diamond oval brooch of open design with four spaced centre collets, set in silver
and gold, c.1820.
£3,000

Photo larger than actual size

Plate 79

Victorian, diamond-set, wild rose spray brooch with rose-bud leaves, c.1840. Note the mount for a detachable brooch fitting showing through the centre.
£5,000
Late 18th century diamond fern brooch, set with cushion-cut diamonds in silver and gold, c.1780.
£5,000

Plate 80

Early 19th century English diamond floral spray brooch, the three flower-heads
'en tremblant', surmounted by two wheat-ears, set in silver and gold, c.1800.
£12,000 — £15,000

(Courtesy of Michael Poynder and Christie's)

Plate 81

Left to right, top to bottom
A set of six Georgian diamond buttons, set and backed with silver, c.1800.
£6,000+
Early Victorian diamond-set brooch in the form of a wild rose, in silver and gold — a delicate setting with a minimum of metal, and showing the naturalism of design that developed at this period, c.1840.
£5,000+
Victorian diamond collet necklace, set in silver and gold, c.1850.
£9,000+
Victorian diamond Maltese cross pendant with brooch fitting, set in silver and gold, c.1845.
£6,000
Georgian diamond five-petalled flower brooch, set in silver and gold, c.1800. Compare the stiffness of design in this brooch to the wild rose brooch above.
£5,500
Mid-Victorian diamond flower spray brooch set in silver and gold.
£7,000

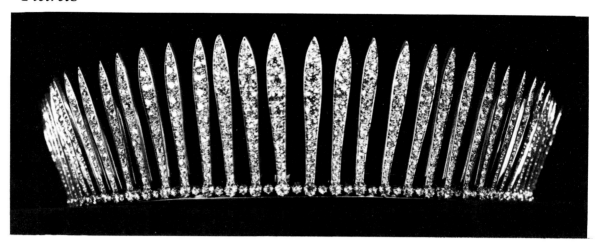

(Christie's)

Plate 82

Early 19th century diamond 'tiara Russe', mounted in silver and gold, and may also be worn
as a 'fringe' necklace.
£25,000 — £35,000
Mid-Victorian diamond tiara, set in silver and gold, c.1895.
£18,000 — £25,000

Paste

Paste is glass, and has been used in jewellery since archaic times to simulate precious stones. Although ancient glass cameos and intaglios have survived, little medieval jewellery in paste appears on the market as, being of nominal value and easily broken, it was discarded.

The combination of two separate events in Europe gave rise to the importance of paste as a type of jewellery. In the second half of the 17th century, the English glass manufacturer, Ravenscroft, discovered lead or flint glass, which, when cut and polished, showed remarkable brilliance and clarity. This was followed closely by the development of the "brilliant cut". In the 1720s a jeweller named Strass combined these two processes and started to produce really good paste jewellery in Paris. In time this was copied by other European jewellers who created many beautiful designs, making pastes in different colours and using tinted foils to simulate the range of colour found in natural gemstones. Fine quality paste rarely appears on the market today, as it has been broken up for the use of the original silver and gold settings. Also it was made only for a comparatively short time between the 1730s and the 1870s. After that date, mass-production techniques meant that the market was flooded with lesser quality articles. However, some French open-backed paste jewellery from the 1920s is noteworthy for its design, and occasionally for the fine hand-made silver mounts.

The quality of setting during the earlier period was extremely high and paste from the 18th and early 19th centuries should not be looked upon purely as costume jewellery, but as jewellery that has a design and an ornamental quality in its own right. The cutting of paste was carried out in the same way as precious stones and the setting and mounting done by the same craftsmen with the same precision and delicacy. Pastes were nearly always brilliant cut, 90% of them being foiled and set in silver. The foiled pieces are essentially closed back. Earlier pastes, in order to simulate the black dot appearance of the culet of a brilliant-cut diamond, when viewed through the table, had a minute spot of black ink or paint put under the base of the paste or on the surface of the foil. Sometimes, coloured pastes are not necessarily pieces of coloured glass, but are colourless, with their back facets painted with the appropriate colour. Foiled paste jewellery, like all foiled jewellery, should never be allowed to get wet, or be cleaned in a liquid, since water will get between the stone and the foil and the brilliant surface of the foil will discolour. This is why so much old paste jewellery appears to be grey and lifeless. Modern paste, after the 1870s is much coarser, flashier, and not nearly so well made. Many of the mounts were stamped out and drilled by machine instead of being individually hand-made. A vast amount has been produced in England and America from the turn of this century onwards and is called "diamanté", or "rhinestone". Paste is often set in conjunction with semi-precious stones and clear crystals.

Technicalities: Flint or lead glass is composed of potash, soda and flint or lead oxide. Lead increases its brilliance and gives it a characteristic greyish tinge. The S.G. varies from 2.5-3.3; hardness around 6, although lead glass is sometimes lower; R.I.: 1.5-1.7. The later paste was more often made of crown or bottle glass which was cheaper to produce.

17th, 18th, & 19th Century Paste Jewellery

(Michael Poynder)

Plate 83

Top to bottom

Late 18th century foiled pink topaz and white paste necklace, set in silver and backed with gold.
£900 — £1,200

French paste open-work button brooch, set in silver, closed back, marked with French control mark for 1798-1809.
£300 — £350

A pair of Stuart pink foiled crystal earrings, the crystal drops suspended from rose-cut white pastes, set in silver, English, late 17th century. Note the style of setting of the circular white pastes, similar to 'cut-card' work styles of late 17th century English silver.
£400 — £500

Mid-19th century crystal and white paste crowned harp, the four large rectangular crystals open-set in silver, the pastes set in silver and backed with gold. Probably made in Dublin by West or Waterhouse about the time of the Great Exhibition of 1851.
£300 — £350

Georgian and Victorian Paste Jewellery

Plate 84 *(see opposite)*

Left to right, top to bottom

Late 19th century harlequin paste necklace, silver-backed, Flemish, c.1880.
£450 — £550

Early Victorian blue enamel and paste button set and backed with silver, one of a set of four.
£275 — £330

Georgian flat-cut garnet and paste clasp, the centre set with an ink on ivory monogram, the whole set and backed with gold, c.1800. *£500 — £600*

Georgian purple glass and paste button, set and backed with silver, c.1810, one of a set of three.
£275 the set

Georgian, green and white paste, pavé set flower brooch, set and backed with silver, c.1830.
£225

Georgian, blue enamel and white paste, oval brooch with a monogram in the centre, backed with silver, c.1800. *£330 — £450*

Georgian foiled amethyst surrounded by white pastes as a brooch, set in gold, c.1820.
£425 — £525

Georgian green and yellow paste locket-frame set in gold, c.1820. *£225*

Georgian oval jardinière clasp, the blue glass overlaid with seed pearls, mother-of-pearl and white paste, surrounded by white pastes, set and backed with gold, c.1785. *£300 — £400*

Georgian green paste cluster brooch with a foiled crystal centre, set and backed with gold, c.1780.
£70 — £90

Early Victorian amethyst paste collet necklace, set in gold, c.1840. *£450 — £600*

(Courtesy of Harvey & Gore and N. Bloom)

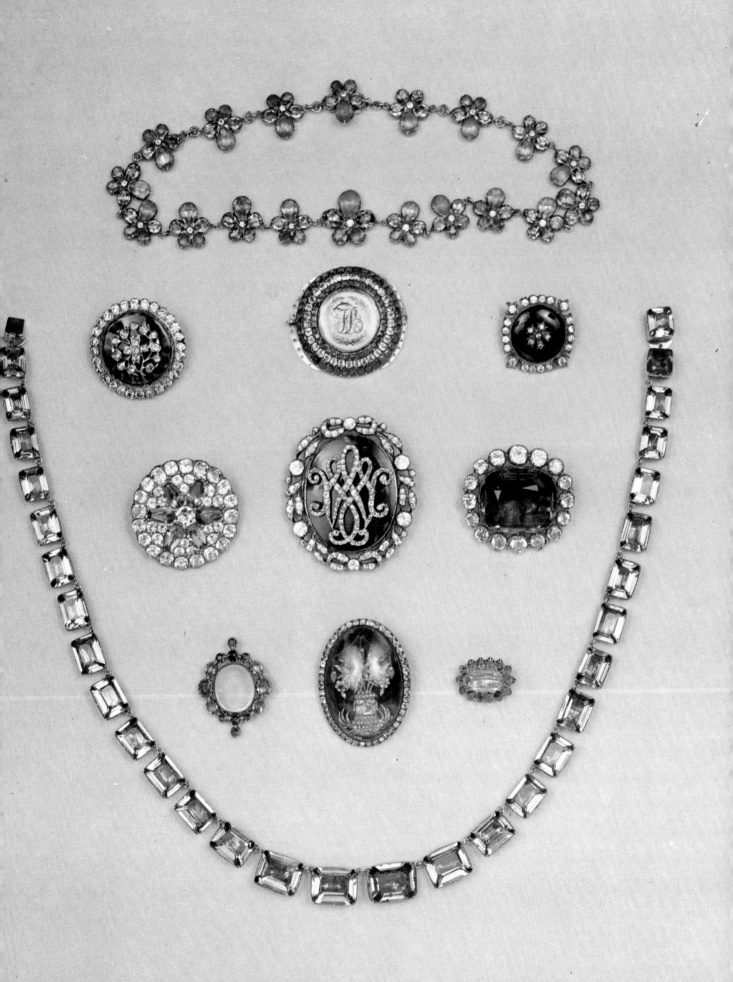

Plate 85

Late 18th century white paste flower brooch, pavé set in silver, foiled and closed back. Actual size 1¾ ins. in diameter (4.5cm), enlarged 6.6 times. The culet of the paste is accentuated by painting in a black ink dot at the time of setting.
£850 — £1,000 a pair

94

Plate 86

Top to bottom, left to right
Paste and enamel Masonic badge, dated
'May 3 1780'
£500
Oval white paste open-work floral brooch,
c.1825
£140
White paste sunburst target brooch, c.1800.
£300
Victorian paste star brooch, c.1870.
£120
Mid-Victorian paste floral brooch with three
drops, c.1850, in the French style of
Lemonier.
£190 — £250
Late Victorian shell-shaped paste brooch,
gold-backed, c.1880.
£120 — £140
18th century paste girandole pendant. The
foiling is dull which accounts for the low
price.
£150
Pavé set paste six-petalled flower brooch,
c.1780.
£475 — £550
Pavé set paste button brooch, c.1800
£150
Perfect late 18th century crystal collet
necklace set in silver and gold-backed,
c.1800. Note pendant ring at bottom centre.
£1,200

(Harvey & Gore)

Paste bracelet clasp, pavé set in silver.
£180
Mid-Victorian paste sunburst brooch,
c.1790.
£400 — £450

Plate 87 *(see opposite)*

Five 19th century paste head ornaments set in metal gilt, all the stones are paste (or glass), imitating pearls, diamonds, turquoises, coral, amethysts, rubies, sapphires and emeralds. One way which helps to differentiate between paste and real stones is to look at the surface lustre. The bright lustre of the 'turquoise' and 'coral' here is too glassy and reflects too much light compared with the real stones, and the 'nacre' of the artificial pearls will peel off, often at the point where they are threaded on to a string, or rub against their setting.
About £250 — £450 each

(Richard Digby)

Ivory

Ivory is a natural bone formation and is normally white, discolouring with age and body grease to a brownish yellow. It is a porous material, although reasonably hard, and forms the teeth of mammals. In some cases these teeth have developed into large tusks, as in the case of elephants, walrus and boars. It has a nerve centre and consequently the sharp end of the tusk or tooth will be solid, and the base hollow.

The major source of ivory is obviously the elephant, both African and Indian, but hippopotamus and hog and several other mammals also have ivory teeth, although their use in jewellery is more limited. The walrus, narwhal and cachalot whale are other sources. The use of ivory became popular with the expansion of British Colonialism in India and Africa, and with the birth of whaling as a commercial industry. Therefore, ivory jewellery and other objects, such as knife handles, became far more common during the Victorian era.

Ivory is seldom faceted and is usually carved in floral motifs, or used in conjunction with other material to form crosses, beads, buckles, etc. Chinese carving is the best in the world, but seldom in jewellery form.

Technicalities: Chemical composition: calcium phosphate. Hardness: 2½. S.G.: 1.70-1.85. R.I.: 1.56. Ivory has been widely imitated by plastics, the most common of which is called ''ivorine''. However, none of these copies can be compared with the fine criss-cross graining of true elephant ivory.

(Richard Digby)

Plate 88

A fine and unusual set of twelve carved ivory Chinoiserie buttons set on a background
of cloth in gold. Late 18th century.
£2,000 — £2,500

(Courtesy of Antiquarius, Bellamy, The Purple Shop and Thesaurus)

Plate 89
Left to right, top to bottom

Faceted ivory bead necklace.
Victorian, ivory buckle inlaid with silver.
Ivory, cherub stickpin, late 19th century.
Ivory, plaque brooch with carved ivory birds on a branch.
Coral-coloured composition ivory link bracelet with Victorian, 9ct. gold and clasp.
Floral, carved ivory cross, c.1855. A fine piece of delicate carving, easily damaged.
Chinese ink-stained ivory bangle.
Carved ivory, horse brooch.
Ivory hand pendant, designed as a châtelaine with gold and gold-plated miniature pendants, c.1870.
Ivory, link bracelet with metal-gilt padlock.
Carved ivory, rose pendant.
Indian ivory bangle with carved lion motif around outer edge.
Ivory, cherub pendant, made in 1975, a good example of modern craftsmanship.
Ivory, rose pendant.
Long carved ivory link chain.
A string of graduated ivory beads. Note the cracking and staining in the latter two, due to 'wear and tear'.
£100 — £250 each

Cameos and Intaglios, 16th to 19th Centuries

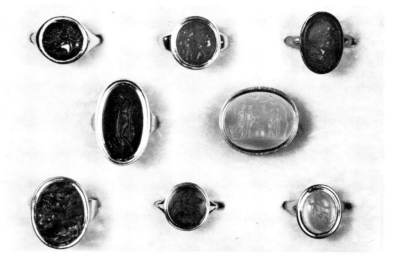

(Wartski)

Plate 90

Left to right, top to bottom
17th century cornelian intaglio of a profile head, set as a ring. *£850 — £1,000*
Classical Greek intaglio in cornelian, two figures, 4th-3rd century BC. *£550 — £850*
Cornelian intaglio ring, profile of a woman. *£450 — £500*
Long oval intaglio ring, jasper, mythological figure, 18th century. *£850 — £1,000*
White agate 18th century intaglio ring of a group of figures. *£550 — £700*
18th century lapis lazuli intaglio of an angel. (Lapis lazuli intaglios are more commonly
found with coats of arms or crests as signet rings.) *£650 — £700*
Renaissance cornelian intaglio ring of a falcon. *£750 — £1,000*
Classical white agate intaglio, a sitting figure. *£550 — £650*

Plate 91 *(see opposite)*

Left to right, top to bottom
A very fine, 18th century, translucent hardstone cameo in low relief, set as a pendant in a mid-19th
century Holbeinesque jewelled and enamelled frame. *£6,000*
Mid-Victorian, profile, portrait cameo, set in a gold frame of entwined leaves with pearls and
diamonds. Note the good use of the colour-banding in the head-dress. *£2,700 — £3,500*
Late 19th century, French, pendant/brooch set with a cameo signed 'Girometti', in a frame of
pearls, rubies, diamonds and lapis lazuli. *£4,500 — £5,500*
Large, early 19th century, hardstone cameo of a mythological scene, set as a pendant in an
Edwardian, platinum and enamel frame, with a platinum and pearl chain. *£3,000 — £4,000*
Mid-Victorian, hardstone cameo suite of brooch (left) and earrings (right), set in hollow gold mounts
with applied gold surface decoration, c.1860. *£2,400 — £3,000*
Classical, hardstone cameo of an Emperor, set in a late 19th century, ruby, pearl and gold mount.
£1,800

(B. Barnett Ltd.)

Plate 92

Left to right, top to bottom
19th century black Wedgwood intaglio ring in a gold mount.
£450 — £550
Black and white glass cameo ring set in gold, c.1790.
£325 — £400
Roman nephrite intaglio in an 18th century gold mount.
£400 — £500
18th century cornelian cameo of Medusa's head.
£725
Agate intaglio of Minerva, 4th century A.D. in a reproduction
18th century gold mount.
£400 — £500
Renaissance cameo head in an 18th century mount, set with
amethysts and citrines in gold.
£650 — £850
18th century agate cameo of a child's face.
£550 — £650
Victorian chrysoberyl cat's eye and diamond cluster ring, set in
gold.
£1,350 — £1,650
Large oval 19th century agate intaglio of Hercules slaying
Antaeus.
£1,200 — £1,400
Roman intaglio, cornelian, set in a gold mount.
£400 — £500
18th century Eastern European silver wedding ring.
£150 — £200
Fine cornelian intaglio of a coat-of-arms.
£500 — £600

(Richard Digby)

Plate 93

Left to right, top to bottom
18th century blue and white Wedgwood cameo of a standing figure.
£65 — £75
Early 19th century composite turquoise cameo of a Classical figure, set in a rose
diamond frame with a fine engraved gold back, French, c.1820.
£1,000
19th century bloodstone intaglio.
£60 — £65
18th century agate intaglio, showing colour-banding (cracked horizontally).
£150
16th century agate cameo of a warrior's head.
£350
18th century agate cameo, the bust of a man.
£350 — £400
Large 19th century oval shell cameo of Medusa's head, with finely carved detail.
£200
19th century coral cameo brooch of a woman, set in gold.
£300
Small 18th century profile cameo in agate.
£300
19th century glass intaglio, by Tassi.
£75 — £100
19th century portrait shell cameo, with fine clear detail.
£90 — £140
Large 19th century shell cameo of the Three Graces, mounted as a brooch in gold,
c.1860.
£350 — £400
19th century Neo-Classical shell cameo in a plain gold mount.
£150 — £175
Fine early 19th century agate cameo of a kneeling figure.
£350 — £400
Early 19th century glass mosaic of Rome, in a turquoise-coloured glass frame.
£150
19th century shell cameo of a group of birds.
£100 — £150
Early 19th century blue and white Wedgwood cameo of Hercules and the Lion.
£200 — £250

Plate 94

Left to right, top to bottom
Cameo of a battle scene, set in a 19th century, gold mount.
£300 — £350
Shell cameo of an angel in a 9ct. scrolled gold mount.
£300 — £350
Early Victorian cameo of Queen Victoria in a gold mount.*£300 — £350*
Hardstone cameo, set in a pinchbeck mount, with pastes as a pendant brooch.
£180 — £220
Mid-Victorian, cameo bracelet of mythological scenes set in a 15ct. scrolled gold mount.
£1,250 — £1,500
Georgian, blue and white Wedgwood double cameo, set in an octagonal, silver frame with a swivel centre.
£270 — £320
A pair of mid-Victorian earrings, the cameos set in gold foliage mounts with gold pendant drops, c.1860.
£350 — £400
A pair of early Victorian earrings, the top cameos of 'grotesques', the long drop cameos of two Muses, set in 18ct. scrolled gold mounts, c.1845.
£850 — £1,000
Mid-Victorian, lava cameo, the profile of a woman, set in gold.
£85 — £100
Hardstone cameo set as a ring in gold.
£220 — £250
Mid-Victorian, bar brooch of engraved gold set with two portrait cameos.
£200 — £250
Cameo of two figures in the Roman style, set in 9ct. gold as a brooch.
£250 — £300
Hardstone cameo set as a pendant in 9ct. gold.
£150 — £175
Hardstone cameo, the bust of a lady, set in a rectangular gold frame of leafy design.
£200 — £250

A comprehensive collection of 19th century cameos, particularly the 'shell' examples in the earrings.

(Courtesy of Antiquarius, Anne Tan, Bellamy, The Purple Shop and Thesaurus)

Mourning Jewellery

Mourning jewellery became popular in the 15th and 16th centuries in England, and the earliest examples prior to the Commonwealth period, 1649-1660, were usually in the form of a head or skull, enamelled in black and white. After the Civil War it was considered a status symbol to wear mourning rings. Retrospective rings were not unusual and at this time many were produced to commemorate the execution of Charles I. In the early 18th century, fine scrolled rings were made, with white enamel when mourning a single person, and black enamel for a married person. The dear one's name, age and dates of birth and death were recorded round the shank of the ring which was set with a diamond, crystal or paste, depending on the pocket of the purchaser. A loved one's hair, plaited and set under thin pieces of crystal or glass, was also used in conjunction with the dates of birth and death inscribed on the inside of the shank, or on the back of a brooch or ribbon slide. The Classical Revival at the end of the 18th century extended into mourning jewellery, and rings and brooches were produced depicting, or even shaped like, funereal urns. Plaited hair would surround an ivory plaque, frequently bearing a portrait of the deceased; and this in turn would be enclosed in a fine frame of blue, black or white enamel set with diamonds, garnets, pastes, pearls, etc. During and after the Regency period, whole suites of jewellery — chains, bracelets, lockets, rings, pendants and brooches — were all made of the finely plaited hair from the head of the loved one. It is strange to note that most of the hair used seems to have been a nondescript brown: fine blonde or jet black hair is not often seen, so one wonders if the hair did in fact come from the individual's head? The sentimental attachment to mourning jewellery during the Victorian era, particularly after the death of Prince Albert in 1861, is seen in terms of jet jewellery, separately discussed, and in the brooches, pendants and rings enamelled in black and actually made to read "In Memoriam" or "In Loving Memory". During Queen Victoria's reign coral and pearls were allowed at court, as half mourning jewellery, and this became popular throughout the country. Fortunately, the fashion for all mourning jewellery ceased after her death.

Cameos and Chains

Plate 95 *(see opposite)*

An unusual, heavy gold-link chain, classical in design, mid-Victorian, c.1860. *£1,500 — £2,000*
A fine, cameo suite of necklace, brooch and earrings, the hardstone cameos depicting mythological scenes and figures, surrounded by green enamel and set in ornate, scrolled gold mounts, the cameos c.1780, the mount Victorian, c.1845. *£6,000 — £7,000*
Fine, gold mesh necklace with a gold snake clasp set with garnets and turquoises, c.1825. An excellent example of fine Georgian gold-work, adapted to the characteristic movement of the animal it depicts. This type of necklace was made in gold or pinchbeck, but once damaged is difficult to repair. *£2,000*

(Harvey & Gore)

Plate 96

Left to right, top to bottom

Charles II memorial ring in gold with a carved shank showing traces of original enamelling, the heart-shaped head with gold thread monogram on blue cloth under crystal, in commemoration of Charles I.

£800 — £1,150

Early 18th century black enamel memorial ring set with a crystal, dated 1736. The scrolled black enamel on gold is typical of mourning rings of this peroid.

£350

Late Georgian seed pearl memorial ring with hair centre, on a carved split shank, dated 1827. Seed pearls denote tears in mourning jewellery.

£350 — £400

Late 18th century marquise-shaped miniature ring depicting a woman and an anchor, drawing with ink on ivory, set in gold. In the late 18th and early 19th centuries many memorial rings are associated with death at sea during the Napoleonic Wars.

£300 — £350

Georgian black and white enamel ring in gold, the shank engraved 'In Memory Of', the head set with jet and a white enamel urn, the reverse inscribed with the remainder of the memorial, and with a hair inset, English, dated 1819, in perfect condition.

£350 — £400

Late 18th century oval memorial ring, the urn detailed in ink on ivory, surrounded with amethysts, c.1785.

£525 — £575

George III ivory monogrammed ring with a white enamel and gold shank, dated 1774.

£450

Early 19th century wide-carved gold band with black enamel, dated 1800.

£450

Georgian diamond memorial ring, a brilliant-cut diamond set as the centre of an urn, surrounded with rose diamonds in black enamel, with a wide gold shank, dated 1802.

£1,750 — £2,500

Late Georgian black enamel ring with red and white enamel crown, the wide shank with a carved gold border, black enamel and gold inscription in mourning for Byron, dated 1824.

£475 — £575

A fine and rare pair of late 18th century black and white enamel oval rings with centres of pale plaited hair, dated 1793.

£700 — £900

(Courtesy Private Collection and Richard Digby)

(Christie's)

Plate 97

Left to right, top to bottom
Diamond, enamel and gold urn ring, the gold shank engraved: 'L'amitié la donne'
£1,500 — £1,750
Diamond, enamel and gold masked harlequin ring, with gold 'chain link' shank.
£1,500 — £1,750
Enamel masked head ring set with rubies and rose diamonds, French.
£2,000 — £2,200
Rose diamond, enamel and gold ring in the form of two doves on a branch, French.
£1,000
Diamond, enamel and gold ring watch set with rose diamonds, French.
£3,000 — £3,500
Paste, gem-set and gilt pendant watch, English.
£1,500 — £2,000
Circular ring watch set with rose diamonds in gold, French.
£2,000 — £3,000
Gold, ruby and enamel ring, the enamel designed to simulate a watch face, but no movement,
the shank engraved 'J'aime à tout heure', French.
£2,000 — £3,000

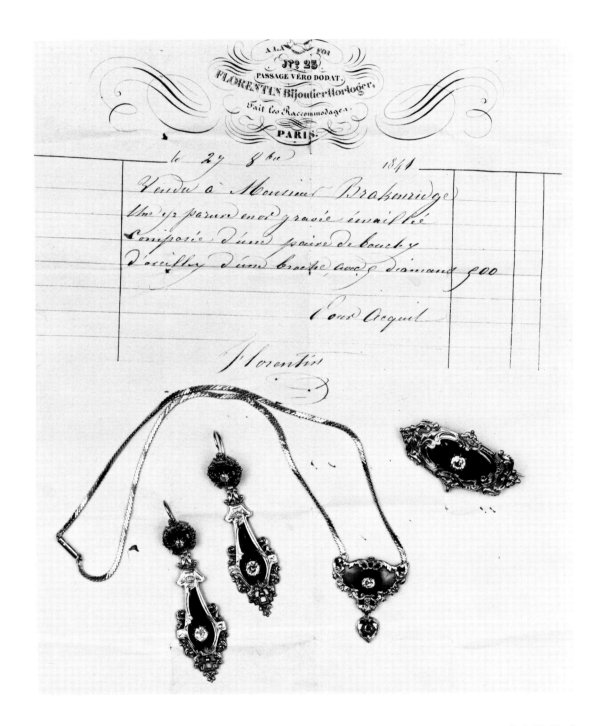

(S.J. Phillips)

Plate 98

Mid-19th century, French suite of memorial jewellery, the brooch, earrings and pendant in black
enamel, set with cushion-cut diamonds in an ornate gold frame of neo-classical inspiration,
accompanied by the original bill of sale, dated 1841.
£2,500 — £3,000

(Courtesy of Richard Digby and Private Collection)

Plate 99

Left to right, top to bottom

Georgian filigree gold heart, the border set with aquamarines, the centre stones of the flowers spelling out 'DEAR', i.e. diamond, emerald, amethyst and ruby. English, dated 1778, with a plaited hair memorial inset in the reverse.

£750 — £1,000

Late 18th century two-colour woven hair heart set in gold, the reverse embroidered with a monogram using hair for thread, c.1780.

£400 — £500

Early 18th century ribbon slide in gold with hair centre, embroidered with a gold monogram and engraved with the same initials on the reverse.

£400 — £450

Early 19th century paste and silver buckle with hair centre and seed pearls, c.1820. This buckle has been converted to a brooch and on the reverse a silver loop has been 'pewtered' on, or soft-soldered; if a hard solder at high temperature had been used, the foil behind the pastes would have been discoloured.

£275 — £325

(Courtesy of Richard Digby and Private Collection)

Plate 99 (reverse)

Late 18th century gold filigree brooch with hair centre which is backed with gold, c.1800.
£225 — £325

Georgian gold heart with hearts stitched on a cloth centre, the reverse monogrammed and dated 1765.
£400 — £500

Late George II memorial heart pendant with hair scrolled and curled in the centre with gold thread, the reverse engraved, dated 1759.
£450 — £550

Late 18th century hair pendant set in a graduated paste frame; the centre is hinged to open on the reverse.
£250 — £300

Plate 100

Left to right, top to bottom
A pair of Indian, ruby and emerald, cloak studs, the reverse (left) enamelled in red, green and white on gold.
£600 — £700
A pair of diamond, pearl and enamel earrings in the form of a fish, the reverse enamelled.
£450 — £550
Foiled crystal, plaque necklace, each crystal in an enamelled frame.
£800 — £1,000
Gold plaque bracelet with hand-painted ivory miniatures of Indian scenes (one of a pair).
£1,500 — £2,000
A pair of Indian, ruby bead, diamond and pearl earrings in gold.
£1,500 — £2,000
Emerald and pearl necklace, with the fine enamelled back shown in the photograph.
£2,000 — £3,000

Indian jewellery is usually mounted in gold with a combination of colourful enamels, precious and semi-precious stones, native-cut or in the form of beads. It is interesting to note that sapphires are seldom used because of superstition about their colour. The design of Indian jewellery is traditional, i.e. styles have not varied greatly over the years and it is difficult to differentiate between modern and antique pieces.

(S.J. Phillips)

Plate 101

Left to right, top to bottom
Victorian black enamel and gold memorial ring, dated 1881.
£80 — £120
Mid-Victorian black enamel and gold memorial ring.
£80 — £120
Georgian half-pearl and hair cluster brooch, c.1820.
£60 — £80
Georgian circular coral and hair cluster brooch, c.1820.
£50 — £75
Dark blue and white enamel and hair centre brooch, c.1825.
£120 — £150
Georgian blue enamel, pearl and ruby snake choker, the body of the snake formed of plaited
human hair, c.1825.
£450 — £500
Early Victorian black enamel, gold and rose diamond memorial brooch, dated 1843.
£220 — £275
Mid-Victorian black enamel brooch inlaid with gold in an ivy pattern, set with a sardonyx,
dated 1874. Ivy is the symbol for eternity.
£180 — £220
Georgian oval scrolled gold memorial ring with hair centre, dated 1818.
£140 — £175
Georgian blue and white enamel marquise-shaped ring with seed pearl flower centre,
formerly a brooch, c.1790.
£150 — £200
Georgian half-pearl cluster memorial ring with two-coloured interwoven hair centre, c.1820.
£160 — £200
Georgian black enamel memorial ring with a gold heart in the centre, dated 1810.
£175 — £200
Georgian gold memorial ring in the form of a belt with a buckle, the belt formed of plaited
hair on a gold shank, c.1830.
£100 — £150
Georgian, marquise-shaped, gold and hair ring, c.1815.
£140 — £170
Victorian gold memorial ring of black enamel with a half-pearl cross.
£110 — £140
Georgian flat-cut garnet and gold locket pendant, c.1780.
£180 — £225
Georgian gold 'witch's heart' brooch with small memorial hair heart, c.1750.
£150 — £200
Late 18th century, marquise-shaped, painted ivory memorial brooch, c.1785.
£120 — £150

(Courtesy of Antiquarius, The Purple Shop, Bellamy, Thesaurus, Tony & Sara)

Coral

Gem coral varies in colour from pale pink to rich deep red, and is the product of a small sea creature called a coral polyp. It is formed in sub-tropical waters and thrives in a narrow temperature range between 13°-16° C.

Coral is graded from white to pale pink — the latter known as Angel Skin — through rose to red; the darkest of all is known as Ox-blood. It was popular with the Victorians and has recently regained favour in modern jewellery design, used in conjunction with such materials as onyx, malachite, lapis lazuli and ivory. In many parts of the world it has long been thought to have magical properties and pieces have been eagerly sought and traded far from its original sources.

The best orange-red colour comes from the Mediterranean around Algeria and Tunisia. It is also found in the sea near Naples, and off the coast of the Italian islands. Another source is Japan. It is usually collected by dredging machines, although divers have always been used.

Coral is usually fashioned into beads, or cut as *cabochons,* and it was very fashionable in the 19th century as a material for the reproduction of classical cameos. Pieces are found in their natural state, rather like small twigs, and are carved into figures, flowers, and fantastic animals, following the natural formation of the piece.

Technicalities: Chemical composition: calcium carbonate, $CaCO_3$. Hardness: 3½. S.G.: 2.6-2.7. R.I.: varies from 1.49-1.65. Imitations are made by staining ivory and various plastics have also been used.

Coral Jewellery

Plate 102

Left to right, top to bottom
Coral bead necklace, *£300 — £500*
Mid-Victorian, carved coral, ram's head brooch set in a scrolled gold mount with acorn drops, c.1855. *£900 — £1,200*
Mid-Victorian gold and coral circular brooch. *£350 — £500*
Coral clasp set with nine beads. *£100 — £140*
Late Georgian, gold filigree brooch with coral centre, c.1835. *£150 — £220*
Victorian, coral cameo clasp. *£130 — £170*
A pair of Victorian, faceted coral, drop earrings, c.1850. *£220 — £275*
Victorian, carved coral, rose spray brooch. It is possible to see the slight colour variation in the coral where successive layers have built up. *£350 — £420*
Fine Victorian, carved ivory hand with a rose, c.1875. *£120 — £160*
Coral cameo in a mid-Victorian engraved gold mount, c.1860. *£280 — £350*
Gold hand, holding a coral rose, as a brooch. *£250 — £300*
A pair of Victorian, coral hat-pins. *£200 — £250*

(Cameo Corner)

(Antiquarius, Thesaurus)

Plate 103

Early Victorian coral necklace, earrings and a pair of bracelets *en suite*, formed
of tiny beads. Jewellery of this type is more commonly made with seed pearls.
It is very delicate and therefore can be difficult to repair.
£600 — £700

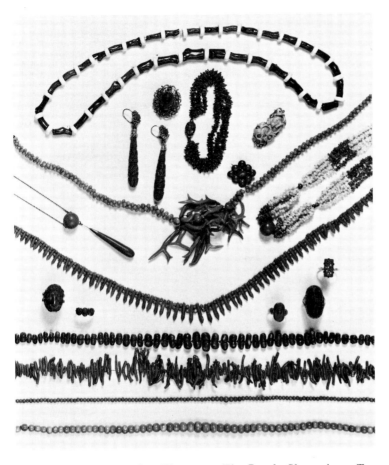

(Courtesy of Antiquarius, Thesaurus, The Purple Shop, Anne Tan and Tony & Sara)

Plate 104

Left to right, top to bottom
Coral necklace with ivory beads.
£150 — £190
Late Georgian, carved coral, drop earrings mounted in filigree gold.
£200 — £260
Late Georgian, coral cameo in filigree gold mount.
£200 — £250
Three-stranded, coral bracelet with coral, cameo clasp set in gold.
£100 — £150
Carved angel-skin, coral brooch in 9ct. white gold mount.
£350 — £425

Georgian, coral brooch set with nine corals.
£45 — £60
Coral, bead necklace with a centre of natural branch coral.
£155 — £200
Late Victorian, coral, drop pendant (perhaps once an earring).
£85 — £95
Georgian, red and white, four-stranded coral necklace, 36ins. (86.4cm) long.
£180 — £225
Early 19th century, coral, fringe necklace.
£100 — £150
Coral ring carved as a lion's face, set in 9ct. gold.
£200 — £250
Georgian, three stone ring set with a coral cameo and two lava cameos.
£85 — £110
Coral, cameo ring in 9ct. gold mount.
£100 — £125
Large, coral, cameo ring set in gold.
£200 — £275
Art deco, coral ring, carved with a floral motif, in rectangular form.
£110 — £140
A string of carved, coral beads.
£100 — £160
A necklace of coral in its natural branch form.
£40 — £80
A string of graduated, coral beads.
£70 — £90
A coral, bead necklace with a gold clasp.
£100 — £160

Emerald, Ruby and Sapphire Rings

Plate 105

Left to right, top to bottom

Victorian, emerald and diamond, three stone ring in an 18ct. carved gold mount, c.1870.
£10,000+

Large, single stone, emerald (4.93cts.) ring in 18ct. white gold with baguette diamond shoulders.
£30,000 — £50,000

Victorian, emerald and diamond, three stone ring in an 18ct. carved gold mount, c.1880.
£6,000 — £10,000

Edwardian, emerald and diamond, three stone ring, the stones collet-set in platinum and yellow gold.
£7,500

A fine Burma ruby of 2.75 cts., mounted as a ring in platinum with baguette diamond shoulders.
£25,000+

Edwardian, emerald and diamond, rectangular, double cluster ring in white and yellow gold.
£1,950 — £2,300

Art deco, ruby, five stone ring with diamond points in a curved rectangular platinum mount.
£3,000 — £5,000

Traditional, ruby and diamond, three stone ring in yellow gold.
£5,500 — £8,000

Art deco, cabochon ruby ring with baguette diamond shoulders, set in platinum.
£3,000 — £5,000

Ruby and diamond, three stone ring, set with a square-cut ruby in 18ct. yellow gold.
£1,950 — £2,350

Large, traditional Victorian, sapphire and diamond cluster ring, the sapphire weighing 7.14cts., mounted in 18ct. gold.
£10,000 — £15,000

Art deco, red tourmaline (rubellite) ring in platinum with onyx and diamond shoulders.
£1,200 — £1,500

Edwardian, sapphire (4cts.) and double-row diamond cluster ring, set in platinum.
£5,000 — £8,000

Large, Ceylond (Sri Lanka), cornflower sapphire (16.35cts.) mounted as a ring with diamonds, in gold.
£25,000 — £30,000

Square-cut sapphire (1.60cts.) and oval-shaped diamond cluster ring, mounted in platinum.
£2,000 — £2,500

Sapphire and diamond, three stone ring in white gold.
£1,500 — £2,000

Large, sapphire, five stone ring containing approximately 6cts. of sapphires in an 18ct. yellow gold mount.
£3,000 — £3,500

(N. Bloom)

Plate 106

Left to right, top to bottom

Early Victorian cabochon amethyst and rose diamond cluster ring with twisted gold and black enamelled shank.

£200 — £250

Georgian single flat-cut garnet ring with narrow twisted gold shank.

£120 — £170

Georgian graduated five stone rose diamond half-hoop ring, set in silver.

£250 — £300

Early Victorian ruby, pearl and emerald ring with carved gold shank, c.1840 (damaged, hence low price, normally more).

£200 — £250

Georgian garnet and grey pearl cluster ring with carved gold shank, c.1830.

£200 — £250

Georgian flat-cut garnet and pearl cluster ring with plain gold shank.

£160 — £200

Georgian crystal ring set in silver and gold.

£200 — £250

Georgian pearl and emerald ring with scrolled gold shank.

£200 — £250

Georgian pearl cluster half-hoop ring.

£200 — £250

Georgian rose diamond cluster ring, set in silver.

£300 — £400

Georgian amethyst and pearl cluster ring with amethyst shoulders.

£220 — £275

Georgian crystal and pearl cluster ring with hair centre and carved gold shank, c.1825.

£180 — £240

Georgian tourmaline and pearl cluster ring with wide gold shank.

£200 — £250

Georgian carbuncle and pearl square cluster ring with split gold shank.

£200 — £250

Georgian ruby cluster ring in filigree setting, 18th century.

£325 — £375

Georgian foiled citrine ring with hollow scrolled gold setting, c.1820.

£180 — £240

(Courtesy of Antiquarius, Thesaurus, Bellamy and The Purple Shop)

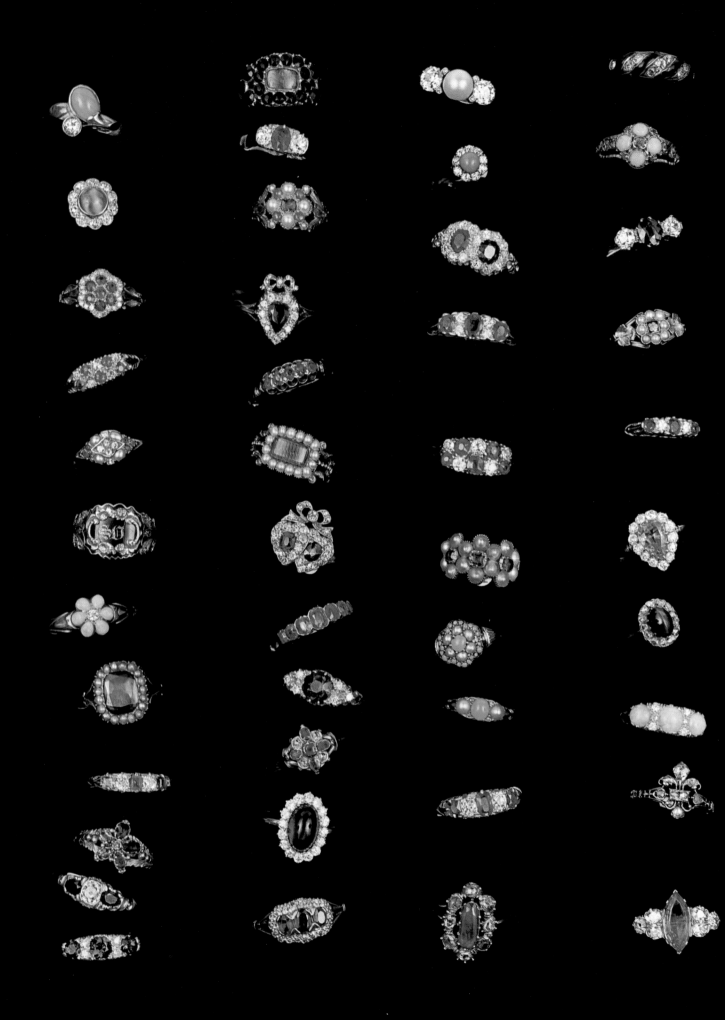

A wide range of 18th, 19th and 20th century traditional rings with a variety of coloured stones:
Top to bottom, left to right
Turquoise and diamond cross-over ring. *£320 — £360*
Chrysoberyl, cat's eye and diamond, cluster ring. *£600 — £950*
Ruby and diamond shaped, cluster ring. *£450 — £580*
Ruby and diamond, double five stone ring. *£400 — £500*
Victorian, ruby, pearl and diamond ring. *£250 — £300*
Georgian, gold and black enamel, memorial ring, dated 1823. *£180 — £230*
Opal and diamond flower head ring. *£230 — £280*
Garnet and half-pearl cluster ring, c.1820. *£270 — £330*
Emerald and diamond, five stone, half-hoop ring, c.1870. *£850 — £1,250*
Late Georgian 'Regard' cluster ring, c.1835. *£300 — £350*
Victorian, sapphire and diamond, three stone ring. *£550 — £850*
Blue tourmaline and diamond, five stone ring. *£350 — £550*
Georgian, hair-work memorial ring, set with jet, dated 1817. *£150 — £180*
Ruby and diamond, three stone ring. *£1,000 — £1,500*
Georgian, emerald, ruby and pearl cluster ring, c.1820. *£350 — £550*
Ruby and diamond heart-shaped cluster ring. *£650 — £750*
Victorian ruby, five stone ring. *£250 — £450*
Georgian, memorial ring with hair-work centre surrounded by half-pearls. *£220 — £270*
Ruby, sapphire and diamond, double-heart ring. *£1,250 — £1,650*
Victorian, ruby, seven stone, half-hoop ring. *£750 — £1,200*
Peridot and diamond, boat-shaped, half-hoop ring. *£380 — £520*
Early Victorian, ruby and rose diamond ring. *£350 — £420*
Carbuncle and diamond, oval, cluster ring. *£450 — £550*
Ruby and diamond shaped, cluster ring. *£600 — £900*
Oriental pearl and diamond, three stone ring. *£750 — £1,500*
Turquoise and diamond, cluster ring. *£450 — £650*
Ruby, sapphire and diamond double-cluster ring. *£1,400 — £2,000*
Ruby and diamond, five stone, half-hoop ring. *£1,200 — £2,000*
Ruby and diamond, double five stone, half-hoop ring. *£1,200 — £1,800*
Georgian, emerald and pearl, triple cluster ring. *£380 — £480*
Turquoise and half-pearl shaped, cluster ring. *£220 — £320*
Turquoise and pearl, three stone, half-hoop ring. *£180 — £220*
Ruby and diamond, five stone, half-hoop ring. *£1,000 — £1,500*
Ruby, emerald and rose diamond, oval cluster ring. *£450 — £550*
Diamond and blue enamel, scrolled, half-hoop ring. *£400 — £500*
Georgian, opal, emerald and ruby ring, c.1830. *£250 — £320*
Sapphire and diamond, three stone ring. *£800 — £1,350*
Late Georgian ring set with a half-pearl cluster in a scrolled mount. *£250 — £350*
Ruby and diamond, five stone, half-hoop ring. *£400 — £550*
Chrysoberyl and diamond, cluster ring. *£600 — £750*
Dark cat's eye and rose diamond, cluster ring. *£400 — £600*
Opal and diamond, half-hoop ring. *£380 — £500*
Georgian, rose diamond, fleur-de-lys ring, c.1780. *£400 — £500*
Marquise-shaped, Brazilian topaz and diamond ring. *£600 — £750*

(Richard Ogden)

Plate 108

Left to right, top to bottom

Victorian diamond, ruby, emerald and sapphire four-banded ring on gold shank, c.1850.
£250 — £300

Early Victorian turquoise and rose diamond ring with scrolled shank.
£250 — £300

Late Georgian pearl and ruby memorial ring, the plaited 'memorial' hair has been removed from the wide gold shank.
£180 — £220

Early Victorian garnet and half-pearl cluster ring.
£200 — £250

Early Victorian cabochon garnet and half-pearl cluster ring with scrolled shank.
£200 — £275

Mid-Victorian black opal ring with shield-shaped mount. The opal is probably a replacement.
£200 — £250

Georgian emerald and rose diamond cluster ring.
£650 — £850

Mid-Victorian pearl and diamond ring, c.1880.
£350 — £475

Georgian white paste and carved gold shank ring, c.1810.
£200 — £250

Georgian pearl and diamond fancy cluster ring, c.1820.
£300 — £370

Georgian rose diamond five-stone ring set in silver, c.1760.
£400 — £475

Mid-Victorian emerald and diamond three-stone half-hoop ring with carved shoulders, c.1860.
£400 — £475

Late Georgian garnet, emerald and pearl cluster ring in scrolled gold mount, c.1830.
£300 — £350

Georgian garnet and half-pearl ring.
£225 — £275

Victorian emerald and ruby double horseshoe ring.
£180 — £200

Early Victorian pink topaz and half-pearl ring.
£250 — £300

Early Victorian turquoise and diamond cluster ring with a scrolled gold mount, c.1840.
£250 — £300

Turquoise enamel and pearl half-hoop ring, c.1870.
£200 — £250

Late Georgian 'Dear' ring, set with half-pearls and a Diamond, Emerald, Amethyst and a Ruby, c.1835.
£275 — £300

Georgian half-hoop ring in gold, set with half pearls.
£180 — £220

(Michael Poynder)

Victorian rose diamond fleur-de-lys ring with centre emerald band, possibly made up from a stickpin.
£225 — £275
Georgian, foiled yellow paste, cluster ring with white paste surround, c.1825.
£175 — £235
Late Victorian sapphire and diamond five-stone half-hoop ring, c.1890.
£450 — £500
Mid-Victorian turquoise and diamond five-stone half-hoop ring.
£300 — £400

Plate 109

Left to right, top to bottom

Five stone, diamond, graduated half-hoop ring in 18ct. yellow gold carved mount, c.1880.
£325 — £475

Late Victorian, five stone ring, set with sapphires, pink and yellow diamonds, in 18ct. gold.
£375 — £475

Mid-Victorian, five stone, coral ring in gold mount.
£190 — £240

Late Victorian, three stone emerald and diamond ring, c.1880.
£250 — £325

Late Victorian, turquoise and diamond ring, in 18ct. yellow gold mount, c.1890.
£125 — £160

Edwardian, diamond, twisted cross-over ring with centre diamond.
£180 — £260

Late Victorian, turquoise and rose diamond, cluster ring in yellow gold, c.1880.
£120 — £150

Late Victorian, emerald and rose diamond, cluster ring in wide yellow gold band, c.1890.
£190 — £225

Victorian, ruby and rose diamond, marquise-shaped ring in 22ct. gold.
£200 — £270

Edwardian, 18ct. gold, emerald and pearl-set ring of elongated form.
£200 — £340

Victorian, 18ct. gold, pearl, turquoise and rose diamond, marquise-shaped ring set in gold, c.1880.
£190 — £250

Turquoise ring set with four spaced diamonds in gold, c.1860.
£210 — £275

Edwardian, pearl and ruby ring with pearl shoulders in 9ct. gold.
£175 — £220

Mid-Victorian, emerald and diamond, three stone ring in ornate, yellow gold, scrolled setting.
£250 — £300

Edwardian, pearl and emerald, banded half-hoop ring in 18ct. gold.
£200 — £240

Mid-Victorian, cluster turquoise ring in 18ct. gold.
£150 — £180

Edwardian, garnet and rose diamond, cross-over ring.
£140 — £180

Late Victorian, peridot and rose diamond, cluster ring in yellow gold, c.1875.
£325 — £400

Late Victorian, carbuncle and rose diamond, cluster ring, set in gold.
£290 — £375

Opal and diamond, three stone, cross-over ring in 18ct. gold, c.1910.
£225 — £290

(Courtesy of Antiquarius, The Purple Shop, Thesaurus and Bellamy)

Garnets

Plate 110

Left to right, top to bottom

Pyrope garnet bracelet, the garnets set in hinged gold sections of four stones, c.1900.
£500 — £600

Victorian oval open circle brooch set in metal gilt.
£50 — £75

Cabochon garnet (carbuncle) stickpin in gold claw setting. Victorian, c.1870.
£100 — £140

Cabochon garnet stickpin in gold scroll setting.
£120 — £150

Late 18th century moss agate and flat-cut garnet brooch, set in silver.
£500 — £600

Georgian filigree gold, flat-cut garnet and Oriental pearl drop earrings, c.1820.
£600 — £750

Mid-Victorian flexible gold bracelet with carbuncle and gold clasp, c.1850.
£1,000 — £1,400

Large carbuncle set in a plain gold circular frame with typical mid-Victorian flexible graduated fringe.
£550 — £650

18th century Spanish flat-cut garnet pendant with cross, and earrings (below left and right) *en suite,* set in gold, c.1775.
£650 — £750

Victorian engraved gold bow with garnet set heart pendant drop, c.1870.
£450 — £550

Flat-cut garnet necklace of floral design set in and backed with gold, the pendant detachable, English, c.1820.
£2,000 — £3,000

(Cameo Corner)

Plate 111

Left to right, top to bottom

Late 17th century, carved wax, reliquary pendant, the gold crown set with garnets and white sapphires or crystals.

£850 — £950

Early 18th century, English, enamel, portrait miniature in a Flemish ruby and rose diamond-set frame.

£1,400 — £1,800

Late 17th century, Spanish reliquary, carved in wax, in a frame of gold and rubies.

£950 — £1,100

Mid-Victorian, enamel brooch of cherubs, in a seed pearl frame, c.1870.

£400 — £600

19th century, cornelian cameo set in a black and white enamel frame of open-work design.

£700

Late Victorian, faceted, rock crystal pendant with a beetle of smoky quartz attached, c.1880.

£270 — £325

Mid-Victorian, glass mosaic of birds and flowers in a gold frame, c.1870.

£630 — £750

Mid-17th century, English, wax, portrait medallion in a pierced silver pendant frame.

£500 — £600

A fine mid-Victorian, painted ivory miniature in a pearl and gold frame, c.1850.

£725 — £750

A fine mid-19th century, French, 'madeira', citrine cameo in the classical style, mounted in a blue enamel, diamond and gold frame, c.1850.

£1,250 — £1,500

Mid-Victorian, 'pietra dura', butterfly brooch of malachite, ivory and agates set in an oval gold frame, c.1850.

£550 — £650

Mid-19th century, sardonyx and enamelled, gold pendant of classical influence, c.1850.

£575 — £675

(Richard Digby)

Plate 112

Left to right, top to bottom
Early Victorian turquoise and gold snake necklace with garnet eyes and rose diamond markings on the head, engraved date 1844. The turquoises near the tail are partly discoloured where they have turned green, probably due to being in contact with scent.
£3,000
Mid-Victorian open-work necklace of turquoises and pearls set in silver and gold, c.1850.
£2,500
Victorian, turquoise and gold claw stickpin, c.1870.
£150
Early Victorian, pavé set, Maltese cross in silver and backed with gold, c.1840.
£400
Mid-Victorian butterfly brooch set with turquoises and rose diamonds in gold, c.1870.
£1,800
Edwardian diamond bow brooch with turquoise centre and a drop turquoise, in silver and gold, c.1900.
£950
An unusual, mid-Victorian, diaper-patterned turquoise and rose diamond locket, c.1860. A lovely example of top quality setting, convex pavé set.
£2,500
Turquoise-set Halley's Comet, 1834.
£110 — £140
Mid-Victorian, gold scroll brooch with circular pendent locket, set with turquoises, c.1845.
£400 — £500
Victorian, turquoise and silver scrolled brooch, with locket behind, c.1880, of indifferent quality.
£100 — £150
Late Victorian, gold leaf brooch, set with turquoises and rubies, c.1885.
£350 — £400
(Cameo Corner)

Berlin Ironwork

Berlin ironwork was produced in Silesia towards the end of the 18th century, at the Royal Foundry, and at Count Stolberg's Foundry. It was made by carving and moulding the shapes in wax, pressing these models into a special fine sand, and then filling the impressions with molten iron. These were left to cool, and then finished by hand. Some pieces incorporated niello work, having fine silver wire set into engraved lines in the iron.

The following passage is quoted from "Metal-Work", edited by G.W. Yapp. "The asserted origin of these curious castings is interesting. When the final struggle commenced between Prussia and Napoleon I, the Prussians were terribly impoverished, and a grand exhibition of patriotism occurred. The men volunteered their services, and the women sent their jewels and trinkets to the Royal Treasury; those who did so received rings or other ornaments with the motto, 'Ich gab geld um Eisen' (I gave gold for iron), and these trinkets are still kept as heirlooms in the families of the donors."

(Private Collection)

Plate 113

A fine pair of early 19th century, Berlin ironwork bracelets, c.1820. Note the quality and detail in the figures and scrolled floral frames.

£750 — £900

(Christie's South Kensington)

Plate 114

19th century, Berlin ironwork necklace and bracelet, signed 'Deveranne', Berlin, c.1850. These examples are similar to the later ironwork illustrated in the Great Exhibition of 1851, and the quality is nothing like that of the bracelets shown in plate 113.
£450 — £600

141

Jade

The term jade refers to two quite separate minerals, known as jadeite and nephrite.

Jadeite is normally a pale to dark green, translucent material, and at best, is brilliant green and almost transparent, when it is referred to as "Imperial Jade". The finest jadeite is extremely valuable. Although green is the normally accepted colour range of jade used in jewellery, it also occurs in a variety of colours from black to mauve, red to pink, cream to white.

The coloration of nephrite is from an opaque dark green, referred to as spinach-jade, through browns, yellows and greys, to a dense white, referred to as mutton-fat jade. The most common form of nephrite is a pale greyish green base-colour heavily flecked with dark green and it is quite easily recognised by the experienced eye. Both jadeite and nephrite are hard materials and difficult to carve; it is surprising, particularly with nephrite, that the early craftsmen were able to produce such intricate and beautiful designs using primitive tools. Something like 75% of jewellery sold as jade is nephrite, and only 25% the more valuable jadeite.

The main source of jadeite is in Upper Burma, in the valley of the Uru River, a tributary of the Chindwin River. It does not appear to have been discovered in China itself. Jadeite from the Uru area entered China at the beginning of the 18th century and the so-called Chinese jades prior to this date, be they in jewellery or fine hardstone carving, are in fact nephrite. Nephrite is found in many parts of the world, and the main source for the Chinese carvers was Turkestan, where it is both mined and found in alluvial deposits as boulders, often of great size and weight. Other sources are Siberia, New Zealand, Silesia, Germany, Italy, Alaska, Rocky Mts., British Columbia, Mexico, Zimbabwe (Rhodesia) and Formosa — and no doubt many other places as yet undiscovered.

Jade is cut in jewellery as beads, "en cabochon", or carved with floral, animal or human motifs which are made into earrings or pendants.

Technicalities:

Jadeite: Chemical composition: sodium aluminium silicate ($NaAl(SiO_3)_2$). Crystal structure: monoclinic, minute interlocking crystals. Hardness: 7. S.G.: 3.30-3.36. R.I.: 1.64-1.67. Jadeite has been imitated by such materials as green agate (Swiss Jade), bowenite, green grossular garnet (Transvaal Jade), and even jadeite itself is sometimes stained to improve the colour, but the staining is only superficial and fades within a few years.

Nephrite: Chemical composition: magnesium calcium silicate with iron ($Ca_2(MgFe)_5(OH)_2(Si_4O_{11})_2$). Crystal structure: monoclinic, interlocking masses of fibres matted together. Hardness: 6½. S.G.: 3.00. R.I. 1.60-1.64. Nephrite has not been imitated so widely as jadeite, since at its best the value is not so high. However, materials such as bowenite and steatite or the grossular garnet may be mistaken for it.

Plate 115

Left to right, top to bottom
A row of dark-green (spinach) jade beads. *£450 — £650*
Variegated green, jade beads. *£1,500 — £2,000*
Circular, mutton-fat jade pendant of open-carved design. *£200 — £300*
Long, carved, apple-green jade pendant with gold mount. *£1,000 — £1,500*
A pair of pale green jade and diamond earrings. *£350 — £450*
19th century, carved, jade pendant of variegated mutton-fat with brownish surface patches.
£400 — £500
A string of jade beads of various colours, illustrating the wide range of possible coloration.
£350 — £500

(Cameo Corner)

Plate 116

Left to right, top to bottom

Late Georgian shell cameo mounted as the clasp of a chain bracelet, c.1830.
£375 — £425

Late Georgian cameo set as a bracelet clasp in a gold filigree and chain link bracelet, c.1830.
£950 — £1,250

Victorian pinchbeck bracelet of hinged plaques with floral and scrolled motifs, c.1840.
£200 — £250

Victorian amethyst paste and pinchbeck bracelet with foliage design, c.1850.
£200 — £250

Early Victorian mother-of-pearl, pink paste and pinchbeck link bracelet, c.1845.
£200 — £250

Georgian pinchbeck mesh bracelet with a 'Regard' clasp in coloured pastes, c.1830.
£200 — £250

Pinchbeck and Gold Bracelets, 1830-1850

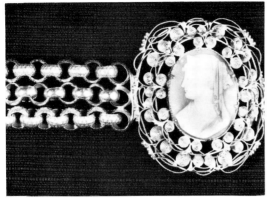

(Cameo Corner)

(N. Bloom)

(Cameo Corner)

(Cameo Corner)

(Cameo Corner)

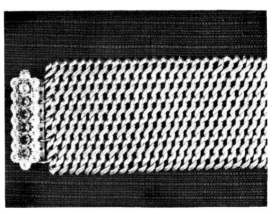

(Cameo Corner)

Plate 117

Top to bottom
Georgian plaque and gold mesh bracelet set with diamonds, rubies, turquoises and pearls in a floral design, c.1820.
£4,000 — £5,000
Late Georgian diamond and sapphire link bracelet set in silver and gold, c.1830.
£7,000 — £10,000
Georgian chrysoprase and three-colour gold bracelet, c.1825.
£2,000 — £3,000
Early Victorian gold bracelet with Wedgwood medallions, c.1840
£2,250 — £2,700
Victorian amethyst and diamond bracelet, c.1880
£5,000 — £7,000
Art deco wide link bracelet set with diamonds, cabochon sapphires, emeralds, rubies and black enamel, c.1925
£25,000 — £35,000
Art deco diamond, cornflower sapphire and crystal link bracelet, c.1925.
£7,000 — £10,000
A magnificent selection of high quality jewellery.

(Harvey & Gore)

Plate 118

Left to right, top to bottom

Early Victorian pinchbeck bracelet, the plaques spelling out 'Souvenir', folding back into book form, c.1840 (both forms shown opposite). A typical piece of the sentimental jewellery popular at this time.

£250 — £350

Late Georgian 'clasped hands' pinchbeck bangle, c.1835 (one of a pair).

£150 — £200 (each)

Early Victorian pinchbeck bangle of foliage scrolls and trellis pattern, set with a pink paste, c.1845.

£150 — £200

Early Victorian pink paste and pinchbeck bracelet of formal *cannetille* work, c.1840.

£150 — £200

Fine Georgian gold link bracelet with *cannetille* work clasp, c.1820. The clasp is detachable and may be worn as a pendant with a special fitting (not shown).

£800 — £1,000

(Cameo Corner)

(Cameo Corner)

(Cameo Corner)

(Cameo Corner)

(Cameo Corner)

(N. Bloom)

Victorian Gold Bangles

Plate 119

Top to bottom
Ruby and rose diamond set, 9ct. gold bangle, c.1885.
£160 — £200
15ct. gold, cast bangle in the Etruscan style, c.1860.
£250 — £300
9ct. gold, engraved bangle in the form of a belt.
£180 — £220
15ct. gold bangle, with applied decoration, c.1880.
£250 — £300
Gold bangle, set with almandine garnets and rose diamonds, c.1875.
£650 — £900
9ct. gold bangle set with a garnet.
£150 — £200
15ct. gold bangle with applied, cross-over decoration, c.1880.
£220 — £270
9ct. gold scrolled bangle, cast.
£220 — £250
9ct. gold bangle set with an amethyst and two pearls, c.1885.
£140 — £160
9ct. gold, slave bangle.
£130 — £160
9ct. gold, slave bangle, hallmarked in Chester.
£150 — £180
9ct. gold, slave bangle.
£130 — £160

(Courtesy of Antiquarius, The Purple Shop, Tony & Sara, Thesaurus and Bellamy)

(Courtesy of Antiquarius, Thesaurus, The Purple Shop and Bellamy)

Plate 120

Top to bottom
9ct. red gold, close curb bracelet, late Victorian.
£150 — £200
18ct. gold open curb bracelet, c.1950.
£220 — £300
9ct. gold curb bracelet, the centre set with turquoises and pearls, late Victorian.
£190 — £250
14ct. gold, snake chain bracelet, c.1930.
£150 — £200
9ct. gold link bracelet, set with amethysts and pearls, late Victorian.
£220 — £260
9ct. gold, decorative open-link bracelet, c.1930.
£150 — £180
9ct. red gold, decorated, hollow-curb, link bracelet.
£150 — £200
9ct. red gold 'gate' bracelet, padlock clasp.
£180 — £240
9ct. gold, hexagonal link bracelet.
£180 — £220
Red and yellow gold, circular link bracelet.
£180 — £220

Plate 121

Eleven late Victorian, silver bangles, some with a gold inlay, or showing Celtic
and Oriental influences in design, c.1880, hallmarked usually in Birmingham,
Chester or Newcastle.
£85 — £200 each

(Christie's)

Plate 122

Top to bottom
19th century bracelet and pendant *en suite,* the pearls, rubies and diamonds set in blue and white
enamel on gold, by Giuliano, c.1880.
£6,000 — £7,000
A good Victorian emerald and diamond hinged bangle set in silver and gold, c.1860; the centre
cluster may be detachable as a brooch. The value of this type of bracelet depends largely on the
quality of the emerald as the diamonds are less important.
£12,000 — £15,000
Large, Victorian, diamond bangle set with three rows of diamonds in silver and gold, c.1850.
This triple row mounting is also a typical ring style of the period.
£18,000 — £25,000

(Christie's)

Plate 123

A set of five, Victorian, flower brooches, the diamonds pavé set in silver and gold, c.1840.
£2,750 — £4,400 each
Victorian, diamond-set, sunburst brooch in silver, backed with gold, c.1870.
£6,000 — £7,500

Plate 124

Victoria, circular, diamond set brooch/pendant of open-work design, c.1860.
Victorian, diamond, target brooch of floral design, c.1855.
Late Georgian diamond brooch in the form of an ornamental cross, c.1830.
Early Victorian, diamond pendant in the design of a floral cross, c.1850.
£3,850 — £5,500 each

Plate 125

Mid-Victorian suite of brooch and earrings set with cushion-cut diamonds in silver and gold, c.1850.
Although this was sold as a suite, the earrings and brooch pendant do not match, as close examination
of the mounting and style will show.
Brooch £6,000 — £8,000
Earrings £6,600 — £8,800

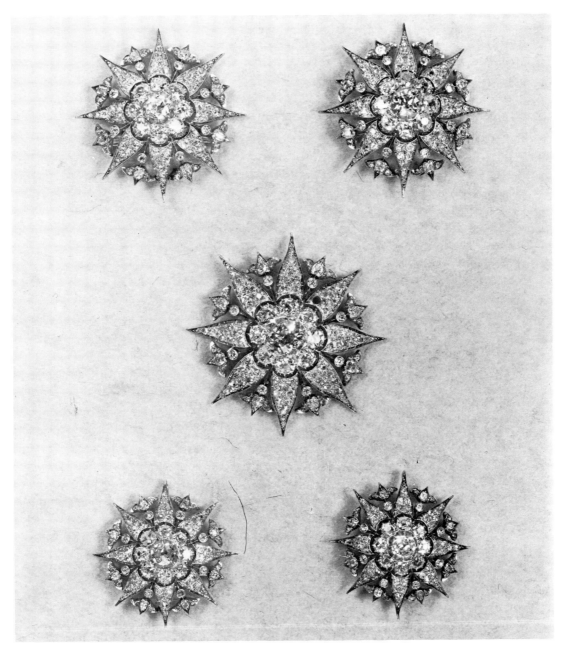

Plate 126

A set of five, eight-pointed, diamond stars with fleur-de-lys between the points, which probably originally formed a tiara, c.1860. Top quality, mid-Victorian mounting and setting, but it is unlikely that these would be kept as a set today, the wearing of one diamond brooch being considered 'enough'.

£6,000 — £8,000

Plate 127

Left to right, top to bottom

19th century, gold, target brooch, c.1860.

£180 — £240

Gold pendant/brooch set with garnets in a scrolled and engraved mount, c.1870.

£450 — £600

Tudor rose brooch in 18ct. gold, by Carlo Doria, c.1865.

£650 — £900

Oval, gold locket with applied anchor, c.1850. The anchor is a symbol for hope.

£320 — £500

Early Victoria, pink topaz and gold brooch of fretwork design, showing classical influence, c.1840.

£550 — £850

Oval, gold locket set with a pearl and corals, c.1860.

£450 — £550

Gold pendant, designed as a ship's wheel, with a centre design of turquoise glass, gold-stone and enamel, c.1860.

£450 — £550

Victorian, gold brooch, the centre designed as a fly, set with a ruby and pearls, c.1870.

£400 — £550

Oval, agate and gold brooch, by Waddesden and Brogden, c.1870.

£650 — £850

Mid-Victorian, gold, hinged bracelet of classical design with a centre circular section set with turquoises and applied gold thread decoration, c.1850.

£850 — £1,000

(Richard Digby)

Plate 128

A mid-Victorian, emerald, diamond and gold, snake necklace cum bracelet, the head having a second clasp opening in order to reduce the length as required, c.1860. A superb example of the goldsmith's work, the feel and sheen of the articulated body is extremely lifelike.
£12,000 — £15,000 very rare

(Christie's)

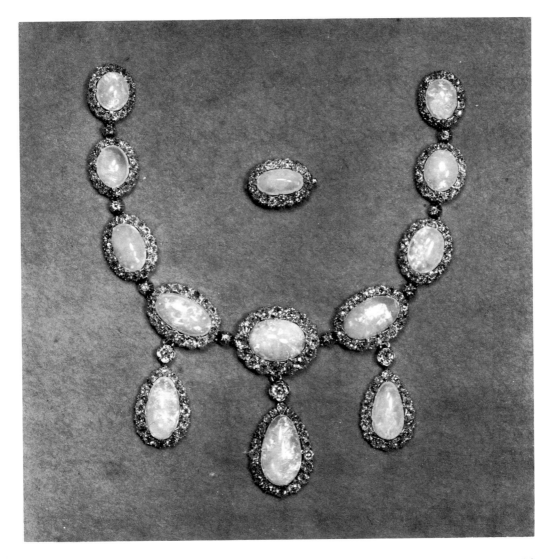

Plate 129

19th century, opal and diamond drop necklace with a brooch to match. English, c.1850.
The oval clusters of the necklace should continue to graduate around the neck but have
been removed, probably to make rings or earrings.
£15,000 — £20,000

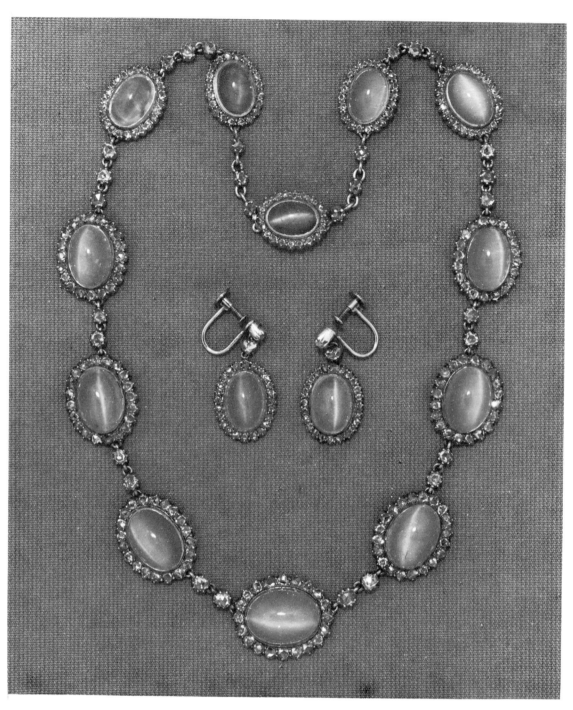

Plate 130

Victorian, quartz cat's eye and rose diamond necklace, set in silver, c.1850. These quartz
cat's eyes are of particularly good quality showing a clear 'chatoyancy'.
£7,500 — £10,000

Plate 131

Mid-Victorian, diamond, fringe necklace, set in silver and gold, adaptable to form a tiara,
c.1870.
£7,000 — £8,500

Plate 132

Mid-Victorian, floral, diamond necklace and earrings *en suite*, set in silver and gold,
which will also form a tiara, c.1850.
£8,000 — £12,000

Plate 133

19th century, Holbeinesque necklace and brooch *en suite,* in blue, white and
crimson enamel, set with rubies, diamonds and baroque pearls, c.1870.
£8,000 — £10,000

Pearls

Natural Pearls

Pearls are formed by very thin layers of a natural secretion from within the body of a mollusc. This secretion, when hard, is known as nacre, and it builds up as a shield around a diseased part or irritation within the shell. Natural pearls are the product of various shells which live either in salt or fresh water. They are normally white, or subtle shades of white; but occasional rarities occur, usually due to disease, and then a pearl can be a steely brown or grey.

The shape, size and colour of the pearl depends on the type of mollusc in which it is formed. Most natural pearls come from the oyster family and are referred to as "Oriental"; in addition, both freshwater mussels and conch shells produce natural pearls, which are referred to accordingly. Freshwater pearls have a different lustre and sheen from the Oriental pearl. Characteristically they are a soft milky white which the experienced eye will distinguish from the richer sheen of the Oriental pearl; both were highly prized in medieval and Elizabethan times. During these periods, Oriental pearls were considered more precious and more costly than diamonds, and were brought to Europe from the Persian Gulf by caravan traders. The weight of pearls is measured in grains, one grain being a quarter of a carat, and it is seldom that Oriental pearls are found in excess of 12 grains. The size of circular pearls is measured in millimetres which makes them easier to grade. The most sought-after pearl is referred to as rosée and has a beautiful pinkish sheen. Obviously the more regular the shape of a pearl, be it round or pear-shaped, the more valuable it is. Pearls formed on the internal surface of the shell, and which do not become fully round, are known as blister pearls. They are usually semi-circular and are mounted in jewellery as button earrings, or as the centre of a brooch.

Pearls are soft and crack easily if they are treated badly. They are easily discoloured by acid, a certain amount of which is contained in all brands of perfume. The natural oils and acidity of human skin can be beneficial or detrimental, depending on the wearer of the pearls. Seed pearls have been widely used in jewellery, usually in cluster form, and this fashion reached its height in the late Georgian period, when suites of jewellery were produced (Plate 137). Seed pearls were sewn in large quantities to finely-cut mother-of-pearl backs with white cat gut. When these backs break, it is very difficult to find repairers to mend such delicate pieces.

Pearls are probably the oldest known gems as they were easily available to ancient man, and did not require cutting or polishing in any way to enhance their natural beauty. Freshwater pearls are found in large mussels which breed in many rivers in Europe. The pearls from the Scottish rivers were highly prized by the Romans, and even today pearls are still found in the Rivers Tay, Dee, Tweed, etc. However, the great traditional source of pearls is from oysters in the Persian Gulf, and from the Gulf of Manaar in Sri Lanka: hence the name "Oriental", a term handed down from medieval times. These pearls are usually small, although occasionally large misshapen ones known as "Baroque" are found and were used as the centre part of magnificent medieval jewels (see Plates 23 and 24).

A very large oyster, as much as one foot across and approximately five times the size of the Persian Gulf oyster, occurs in the South Pacific and off the coast of Australia, and produces large pearls. The conch shell produces a fine pink pearl and is found in the waters of the Gulf of Mexico. However, conch pearls are not often seen in jewellery and have been simulated by light pink coral, stained ivory or porcelain.

Cultured Pearls

Cultured pearls are produced by molluscs in exactly the same way as Oriental or natural pearls, except that the process has been aided by man. The idea of inserting a piece of grit, and more latterly a bead made of glass, plastic or wax, into the shell had been thought of in principle long before Mr. Mikimoto first patented his cultured pearls in Japan around 1915. His discovery of how to open the two halves of the natural shell, without damaging the hinge, enabled him to insert different-shaped beads, which would then become covered by nacre and form pearls indistinguishable from Oriental pearls — except by laboratory tests. The method used to produce these pearls has meant that millions of women have been able to enjoy wearing pearls, that to all intents and purposes are as good as Oriental pearls, but at a fraction of their cost.

However, in 1976 it is interesting to note that the pearl producers in Japan are so worried about the effects of pollution in the sea and air, that the future of the cultured pearl industry is considered to be at risk. Taking this into account, together with escalating production costs, the price of cultured pearls has taken off in the last year. Obviously, this applies mainly to the large sizes of excellent quality. Cultured blister pearls can attain large sizes and are known in the trade as "mabé" pearls ("mabé" meaning half in Japanese).

Freshwater pearls have been produced, particularly from Lake Biwa where they are of a type known as non-nucleated. This means that tissue, which later disappears, has been inserted to cause the irritation within the shell, and subsequently the pearl forms and appears to have no artificial centre bead, unlike the normal cultured pearls. These pearls are round, tending to be baroque and rather flat oval shaped, with a stronger lustre than the natural pearl, but whiter in colour.

Apart from the main source which is Japan, Australia also produces cultured pearls. They come from the very large oysters already mentioned, and pearls in excess of 20mm have been recorded, although at this size they are extremely expensive.

Artificial pearls were far more popular before cultured pearls came within the price range of ordinary women. They were first made in the 17th century, when it was discovered that wax beads could be covered with a product of fish scales which was known as "essence d'orient". Another early type of artificial pearl was made of glass which was then filled with wax. Plastic or wax-coated beads can readily be identified from Oriental or cultured pearls by gripping them lightly between the teeth and rubbing the surface against the sharp edge of a tooth. The artificial pearl will always feel smooth, whereas nacre grits very finely. Artificial pearls are considered to be costume jewellery and are not illustrated.

Technicalities: Chemical composition: aragonite and conchiolon. Hardness: 3½. S.G.: 2.60-2.78. R.I.: 1.54. Natural and cultured pearls can be difficult to distinguish. The only sure way is to have them laboratory-tested where they will be X-rayed. This will reveal the false centre of a cultured pearl.

Cultured Pearls

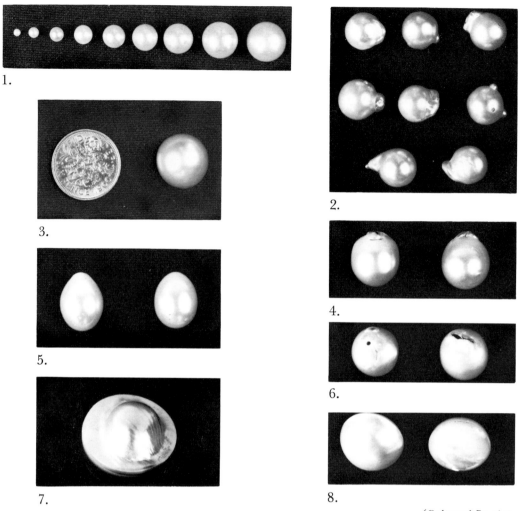

(Cultured Pearl Company)

Plate 134

1. 2mm — £3, 3mm — £6, 4mm — £11, 5mm — £20, 6mm — £38, 7mm — £65, 8mm — £100, 9½mm — £440, 10½mm — £825. Japanese pearls seldom exceed 10½mm.

2. Eight baroque shaped cultured pearls showing irregularities in their formation.
£35 — £45 each

3. 14½mm cultured pearl from the South Seas, photographed with a sixpenny piece.
£3,150

4. A pair of South Sea pearls showing a growth formation which can be disguised in mounting.

5. A pair of South Sea cultured pearls, drop-shaped, 15½mm x 12mm, of good quality.
£7,000 (the pair)

6. Side view of No. 4, South Sea pearls with growth formation.

7. Mabé pearl cut from the shell of the oyster, before trimming.

8. A pair of mabé pearls, left one as seen normally, right one showing the base which was attached to the inside of the oyster shell, now smoothed off and covered with mother-of-pearl to finish it.
£450 (the pair)

Plate 135

A six-row, graduated, Oriental pearl necklace.
£20,000 — £30,000

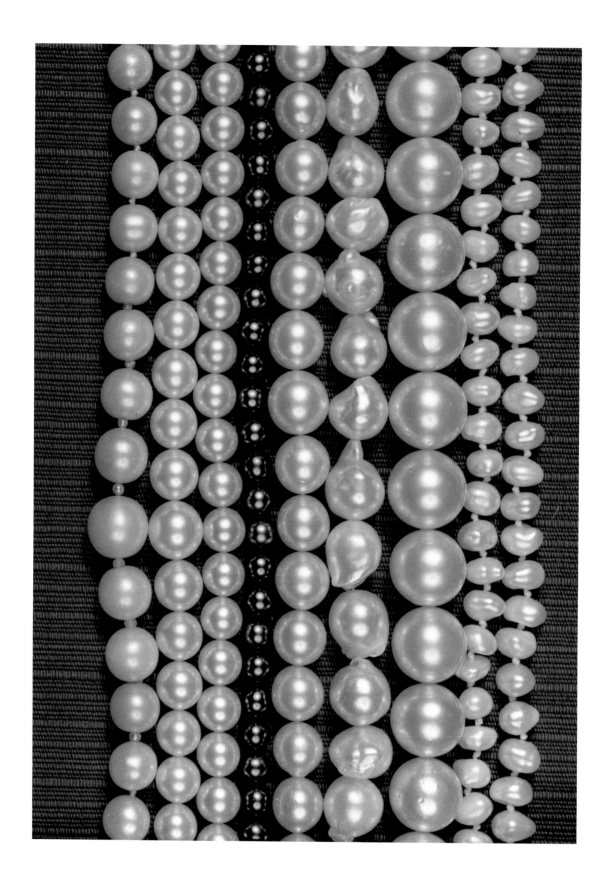

Plate 136

Left to right
(Necklaces averaging 16in. lengths.)
Natural freshwater pearls.
£6,000 — £8,000
Rosée-coloured cultured pearls of graduated size but regular shape.
£2,500 — £3,000
Cream-coloured cultured pearls, uniform shape and size.
£2,000
Cultured black pearls.
£750 — £1,200
Cultured pearls, of large size.
£5,000
Baroque pearls, a variety of irregular formations.
£600 — £900
Exceptionally large South Sea pearls.
£20,000
Double string of non-nucleated cultured pearls from Lake Biwa in Japan. The squashed 'bun' shape and high lustre is typical of these pearls.
£450

(Michael Poynder and Cultured Pearl Company)

Plate 137

An attractive Georgian seed pearl suite of brooch and necklace
of oak-leaf design, c.1800. The photograph of the reverse (below)
shows the mother-of-pearl back which has been cut out in the design
required and the seed pearls were then sewn on with cat-gut. This
type of work can be difficult to repair, since it is very fine and
fragile, and the mother-of-pearl back can crack and break.
£450 — £800

Plate 138

A graduated, Oriental pearl necklace, the pearls of very large size, with a
cushion-cut diamond, collet clasp.
£50,000 — £80,000

(Christie's)

Plate 139

19th century, Oriental, black pearl necklace, with a black pearl and diamond cluster clasp.
This necklace was formerly in the possession of King Ferdinand of Spain.
£100,000 — £200,000
19th century, black pearl and diamond brooch with drop.
£100,000 — £200,000

(Cameo Corner)

Plate 140

Left to right, top to bottom
Emerald and pearl circular brooch in gold mount, c.1870.
£1,500 — £1,800
Gold, marquise-shaped pendant with fringe, set with pearls and a turquoise,
enamel centre, c.1860.
£650 — £850
Blue enamel, target brooch, set with a cabochon amethyst and seven half-
pearls and applied gold-work scrolled design, c.1870.
£550 — £650
Citrine and gold brooch, the citrine set in a gold frame, ornamented with
birds and flowers, c.1865.
£750 — £900
Scrolled gold brooch of open-work design set with aquamarines, c.1870.
£750 — £850
A suite of brooch and earrings, set with cabochon amethysts and pearls, with
applied gold decoration, c.1860.
£1,100 — £1,500

Plate 141

Left to right, top to bottom
Brooch and earrings of coral, pearls and turquoise enamel set in an 18ct. gold mount of classical influence, c.1850.
£900 — £1,100
Gold, knotted rope brooch with a pavé set turquoise centre and gold tassels, c.1845.
£650 — £750
Green garnet and chrysoberyl, target brooch, set in gold, c.1900.
£850 — £950
Pink topaz and emerald brooch in scrolled gold setting, c.1845.
£800 — £950
Blue enamel and diamond, monogrammed shield in an open, floral, gold mount, c.1880.
£600 — £750
Scottish, engraved gold brooch, set with three 'cairngorms' (citrines), c.1870.
£400 — £500
Coral, pearl and gold long drop pendant, c.1880.
£600 — £700
A pair of gold gold swing earrings of classical style, c.1850.
£400 — £500
Circular, gold brooch with applied thread decoration, set with a citrine and pearls, c.1870.
£550 — £650
Oval, gold and amethyst clasp, c.1850.
£200 — £300

(B. Barnett Ltd.)

Mosaic and Inlay Jewellery

Mosaic jewellery was fashionable throughout the 19th century due to the classical revival and the influence of original Greek and Roman examples. The method of making a mosaic is to use small sections of fine rods of coloured glass which are glued into patterns or pictures within a frame of hardstone or coloured glass. The whole piece is then set in an outer gold frame which gives added protection to the fragile centre. Classical architecture, landscapes, and even pet dogs, horses, exotic birds and insects were all popular subjects.

Hardstone, inlay jewellery is often known as Florentine work. The art of the 18th century snuffbox makers and ébénistes was taken a step further in the development of jewellery. Small pieces of differently coloured agates, lapis lazuli, malachite, turquoise, ivory and coral were cut into shapes to make up the required motif, which was set in carved or flat black marble and mounted in gold or silver, and sometimes in jet.

19th Century Enamel, Mosaic and Pietra Dura

Plate 142

Left to right, top to bottom

A pair of mid-19th century, Swiss, enamel earrings, the drops reversible (as shown), set in gold, c.1850.

£650 — £1,200

Mid-Victorian *pietra dura* and goldstone butterfly brooch set in an ornate gold frame, c.1860.

£550 — £650

Victorian, rectangular *pietra dura*, or 'Florentine work' brooch, set in silver.

£180 — £300

A fine, 19th century, Swiss, enamel landscape set in an ornate gold frame attached to a flexible gold bracelet, c.1850.

£1,200 — £1,700

Mid-19th century, *pietra dura* brooch and earrings *en suite,* set in gold, c.1850.

£1,000 — £1,200

Early Victorian, floral mosaic brooch and earrings in black glass, contained within a decorative gold mount, c.1840.

£800 — £1,200

Mid-Victorian, architectural mosaic, set in a flexible gold bracelet, c.1850.

£1,100 — £1,500

(Cameo Corner)

Plate 143

Left to right, top to bottom
Georgian diamond Maltese cross brooch, set in silver and backed with gold, c.1790.
£3,850 — £5,000
Early 18th century pale emerald and rose diamond bow with pendent cross, in silver, the emeralds clear-set.
£3,850 — £4,650
Georgian Maltese cross pendant of agate and three-colour gold, made as a gift for Caroline Mary Gardiner, December 1817, with 'From the Prince Leopold' engraved in gold on the reverse centre section, the locket containing a piece of hair.
£1,650 — £2,200
Mid-Victorian onyx, pearl, turquoise and enamel cross, c.1870.
£350 — £450
Fine, early 18th century, diamond pendant cross, set in silver and gold with a large rectangular-cut centre diamond.
£5,500 — £6,500
Victorian lapis lazuli and gold stylised cross, c.1860.
£1,100 — £1,650

(Michael Poynder)

(Christie's)

(Michael Poynder)

(N. Bloom)

(Christie's)

(N. Bloom)

181

Plate 144

Left to right, top to bottom
Georgian, cut steel cross, metal-backed.
£30 — £50
Mid-Victorian, open-work diamond cross in gold, c.1860.
£450 — £550
Mid-Victorian, pavé set, Bohemian garnet cross in gold, c.1860.
£150 — £200
Early Victorian, Brazilian topaz cross set in 18ct. gold, with a locket back, c.1845.
£650 — £750
Mid-19th century, Hungarian cross, set with amethysts, pearls and enamel in silver, c.1860.
£350 — £450
Early Victorian, 15ct. three-colour gold cross set with a topaz and four turquoises, dated 1840.
£650 — £850
19th century, Italian mosaic cross in the form of a bird with flowers, set in silver.
£85 — £125
19th century, Hungarian, stylised cross set with garnets, turquoises and enamel in silver-gilt.
£150 — £200
Six square-cut amethysts set as a cross in silver-gilt collets.
£100 — £150

(Courtesy of Antiquarius, Thesaurus, Anne Tan and Tony & Sara)

Plate 145

Left to right, top to bottom
Sardonyx cross, metal-backed,
c.1870.
£40 — £70
Large sardonyx cross set with
9ct. gold, c.1865.
£75 — £100
Sardonyx cross with 9ct. gold
pendant fitting, c.1870.
£30 — £40
Ornate niello cross, c.1880.
£60 — £80
Mother-of-pearl cross set in
silver.
£20 — £30
Carved, serpentine cross,
mounted with metal.
£20 — £25
Enamelled cross, set in metal,
made in Birmingham, c.1860.
£15 — £25
Open-work, silver cross set with
moonstones, arts and crafts,
c.1910.
£110 — £160
Plain hollow 9ct. gold cross.
£60 — £85 scarce

(Courtesy of Antiquarius, Tony & Sara, J. Riffel of Thesaurus and The Purple Shop)

Coptic Crosses

(Antiquarius, Stall M1)

Plate 146

A collection of traditional Coptic Crosses in silver, all early 20th century. The Copts were a sect of early Christians in Egypt. The four birds in the bottom cross are said to represent the four apostles.
£40 — £70 each

(Antiquarius, Thesaurus)

Plate 147

Hand-painted, porcelain, sentimental miniature in a twisted silver frame, c.1870.
£150 — £250
Cherub brooch in a 15ct. gold frame, c.1870.
£200 — £250
Miniature of a girl in a jet and silver frame, c.1870.
£150 — £200
Rectangular brooch of an archer, in a gilt metal frame, c.1870.
£140 — £160

Victorian Gold Brooches, 1850-1870

(Cameo Corner)

Plate 148

Left to right, top to bottom.
A pair of mid-Victorian, gold link bracelets with quatrefoil central motif, c.1860 (top and bottom of picture).
£1,400 — £1,800 pair
Gold brooch of open design, in the form of an intertwined ivy spray, c.1870.
£500 — £600
Gold, linked circles brooch with applied thread decoration, c.1865.
£400 — £450
Oval, gold brooch of classical influence, with a matt finish, c.1865. The matt finish was achieved by gilding the gold.
£450 — £550
Gold brooch and earrings *en suite,* a stylised ribbon knot with pendent articulated tassels, c.1855.
£750 — £1,000

Plate 149

Left to right, top to bottom, varying in price from:—
£180 — £350 each
15ct. gold locket, set with a carbuncle and a pearl, c.1860.
18ct. gold target brooch, die-cast and set with corals, c.1860.
18ct. gold, target brooch, cast with applied decoration, set with pearls in a centre star, c.1860.
18ct. gold lozenge-shaped brooch, cast and with applied decoration, set with a diamond, c.1865.
18ct. gold brooch, cast and applied circular motif.
18ct. gold brooch, cast and applied decoration.
18ct. gold brooch with applied oak-leaf decoration.
18ct. gold oval brooch, cast, of good quality.
18ct. gold oval brooch.

(Courtesy of Antiquarius, Tony & Sara, The Purple Shop and Thesaurus)

187

(Christie's)

Plate 150

A set of five, Victorian, diamond butterflies set in silver and gold, worn individually or on a frame
as a tiara, c.1875.
£15,000 — £20,000 set

Plate 151

A pair of late 19th century, diamond brooches in the form of trails of wistaria, set in silver and gold, each section hinged for flexibility. Difficult jewellery to wear but typical of the period when it was fashionable to wear as many diamonds as possible.

£15,000 — £25,000 pair

Plate 152

19th century, emerald and diamond stomacher of open-work design with pendent drop. This is probably a matched-up piece, since there is a difference in the setting of the bow and the centre of the pendant, top c.1880, the centre of the drop c.1830. This unwearable piece would probably be broken up today, the emeralds re-set as fine, large, cluster rings, and the remaining diamonds used by a jeweller as and when needed, and the mounts melted for scrap.

£25,000 depending on emeralds
Late Georgian, turquoise and rose diamond stomacher, set in silver and gold, c.1810. The flecks of matrix (parent-rock) can be seen in some of the turquoises.
£3,000 — £3,750

(Christie's)

190

Plate 153

A late Victorian, diamond necklace, convertible to a tiara, c.1895.
£10,000 — £15,000

Plate 154

1. Victorian, pavé set diamond and sapphire, five-pointed star brooch set in silver and gold, c.1870.
£3,300 — £3,900

2. Victorian, triple-row, diamond crescent brooch, the diamonds cushion-cut, set in silver and gold, c.1870.
£2,000 — £2,400

3. Large Victorian, diamond, six-pointed star brooch set in silver and gold, with a single diamond collet between each point, c.1875.
£1,800 — £2,200

4. Victorian, circular, floral diamond brooch, set in silver and gold, c.1870.
£1,500 — £2,000

5. Victorian, diamond, crescent brooch set in silver and gold, c.1870.
£950 — £1,150

6. Georgian, diamond and rose diamond, circular, open-work daisy brooch, set in silver and backed with gold, c.1820.
£600 — £750

7. Early Victorian, diamond spray brooch set in silver and gold, c.1840.
£1,750 — £2,000

8. Early Victorian, diamond crowned, double witch's heart, set in silver and gold, c.1855.
£1,450 — £1,800

9. Diamond, target brooch, set in silver and gold, c.1860.
£2,000 — £2,400

(Michael Poynder)

1.   2.   3.

4.   5.   6.

7.   8.   9.

The proportions of these brooches have been distorted and give a false idea of value size to size as illustrated.

(Cameo Corner)

Plate 155

A collection of Georgian and Early Victorian hair jewellery, made from woven hair with gold or metal fastenings and decorations as necessary. Hair is much stronger than might be expected when plaited and woven in this fashion.

£100 — £250 per piece, depending on size

(£350 necklace)

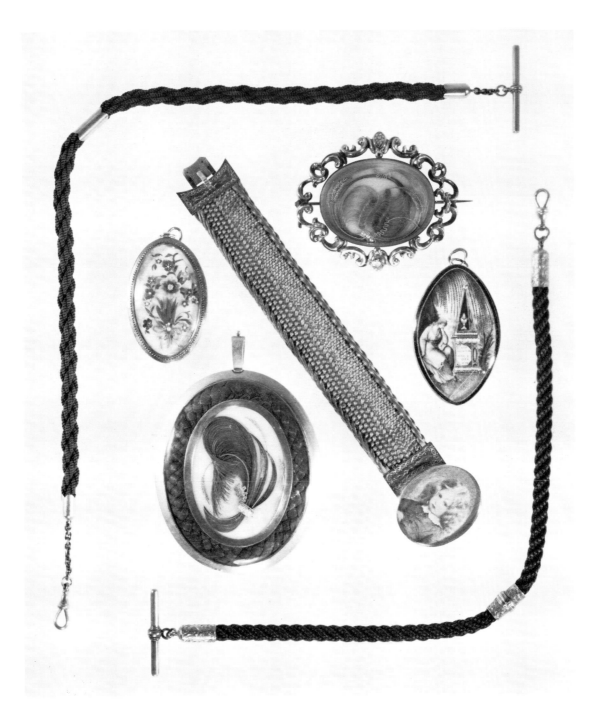

Plate 156

A group of early 19th century gold mounted hair set jewellery in the form of pendants, brooches,
a bracelet and two Alberts.
£290 — £650 each piece

(Antiquarius, Tony & Sara)

Plate 157

An unusual, 19th century bracelet and earrings made of drawn cat-gut, in imitation of the hair
jewellery of the early 19th century.
£75 — £125

(Private Collection and Antiquarius, The Purple Shop)

Plate 158

A pair of gold earclips with fine mosaic flies, c.1860.
£400 — £600

Mosaic pendant with three pendent drops, set in a gold frame. The fine quality of the mosaic in the two pieces above is enhanced by iridescent pieces of glass incorporated in the design which simulate the natural iridescence of insects' wings.
£700 — £800

Real scarab necklace, the scarabs of a greenish iridescent colour, set with amethysts on a 9ct. gold and pearl necklet, c.1880.
£420 — £550

Vauxhall Glass, Bakelite and Bog Oak

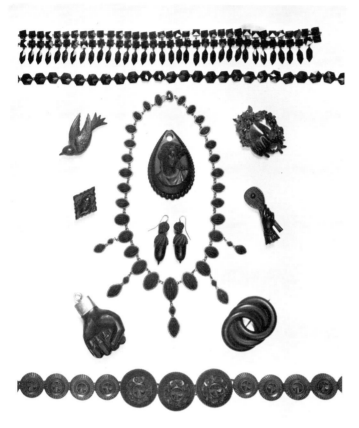

(Courtesy of Antiquarius, Tony & Sara,
Thesaurus, and The Purple Shop)

Plate 159

Top to bottom, left to right
Vauxhall glass, fringe necklace.
£50 — £150
Vauxhall glass, hexagonal, collet
necklace.
£50 — £150
Bog oak, bird brooch.
£50 — £150
Necklace of bog oak in gilt metal with
pendent drops.
£50 — £150
Bakelite cameo pendant.
£50 — £150
Bog oak hand and floral wreath
brooch.
£50 — £150
Bakelite diamond-shaped beetle
brooch.
£50 — £150
A pair of mid-19th century, bog oak
earrings in the form of acorns.
£50 — £150
Bakelite hand with racket brooch.
£50 — £150
Stained wood and silver hand
pendant.
£50 — £150
Bakelite, triple circle brooch.
£50 — £150
Carved bog oak necklace.
£50 — £150

(Cameo Corner)

Plate 160

Lava bracelet of carved links, the clasp formed by two hands and an angel's head, c.1850.
£320 — £550
A pair of lava, cameo, drop earrings, c.1850.
£150 — £200
A large, Victorian, lava cameo brooch of a cherub with a basket, in a scrolling open-work gold frame, c.1845.
£500 — £650
A lava cameo brooch of a woman, in a plain oval mount.
£140 — £190
Lava cameo plaque bracelets, c.1845.
£500 — £800 pair depending on gold or pinchbeck set

The three bracelets illustrated indicate the variety of shades in which lava is found, varying from pale yellows and greys to pale pinks, darker greys and browns. The colours are always muted and the surface matt, taking little polish.

199

Tortoiseshell

Tortoiseshell is the natural shell of the sea-going turtle, and has nothing whatever to do with tortoises. The shell is dark brown to yellow, usually mottled, and because it is easily worked and takes on a pleasant shine when polished, it was much used in 19th century jewellery. Tortoiseshell jewellery was sometimes inlaid with gold or silver piqué work in geometric patterns and designs. Wet, tortoiseshall is very malleable and when pressed into moulds and carefully dried, the resulting cameo effects will be permanent. Moulded tortoiseshell was used in mid-Victorian earrings, lockets, chains and small boxes. The colour of tortoiseshell is enhanced by cutting it thinly and backing it with gold or red foil. It was also used for the fashioning of combs and snuffboxes, and as an inlay for furniture.

The turtle which produces tortoiseshell lives in the warm waters of the Pacific Ocean and the West Indies.

Technicalities: Hardness: 2½. S.G.: 1.29. R.I.: 1.55. Tortoiseshell is frequently imitated by Bakelite and other plastics.

Plate 161

19th century Victorian piqué tortoiseshell jewellery, inlaid with gold and silver in intricate designs, as brooches, buttons, earrings, buckles, pendants. etc.
£150 — £450 per piece

(Cameo Corner)

Victorian Tortoiseshell and Piqué Work

(Courtesy of Antiquarius, The Purple Shop, Anne Tan and Thesaurus)

Plate 162

Left to right, top to bottom
A pair of silver and piqué earrings.
Silver and gold piqué, Maltese cross brooch.
Hexagonal silver and gold piqué brooch.
Tortoiseshell, link bracelet with tortoiseshell and silver padlock fastening, c.1875.
Carved tortoiseshell, link chain with pendant locket, the front carved with a beetle.
A pair of tortoiseshell, gold and rose diamond set combs.
A pair of carved tortoiseshell, urn earrings, c.1860.
Carved tortoiseshell, locket pendant with a mirror in the centre.
Tortoiseshell and silver decorated bangle.
Blond tortoiseshell chain.
£150 — £450

Scottish Pebble Jewellery

Queen Victoria inadvertently attracted tourism to Scotland when she set up household at Balmoral in the 1840s. Her move, coupled with the development of the railways, gave the Scottish Season popularity and triggered off all the normal money-making projects we associate with the tourist industry today. Not least was the manufacture of local jewellery.

Agate and granite is found in many parts of Scotland and when small pieces are cut, faceted and polished, the resultant range of colour can be put together in pretty shapes and forms — from traditional "plaid" pins to thistles (the national emblem), buckles, necklaces, etc., as in Plate No. 163.

The mounts for the pebbles were usually hand-made in silver, although expensive suites were also produced in 18ct. gold. This form of "souvenir" jewellery rapidly became fashionable and soon, to meet demand, the silver mounts were produced in Birmingham by diecasting and therefore bore the Birmingham hallmarks. Naturally the standard of workmanship suffered accordingly. The fashion became so popular in the latter part of the century that pebble jewellery was even exported to France and Germany. This further demand in the industry resulted in complete pieces being made in Birmingham, often in ignorance of the range of stones involved. Hence some examples have apparently inexplicable pieces of malachite and Connemara marble included in the designs, neither of which occur north of the border. Scottish tourist jewellery extended into printed tartan papier mâché and tin strung on elastic to make cheap bracelets, etc., to cater for even the humblest purchaser.

The only semi-precious stones found in Scotland are of the quartz family. Yellow brown and reddish quartz are called "Cairngorms" but are really citrines in gemmological terms. These stones were cut and polished in the same way as any other stones and set in conjunction with the plaque for faceted "pebbles". Poor quality amethyst (pale purple quartz) was also used.

The original firms to make top quality pebble jewellery were Makay and Cunningham of Edinburgh and Muirhead of Glasgow, whilst Reffie of Aberdeen produced larger, coarser pieces, usually set with granites.

Scottish Agate "Pebble" Jewellery, c. 1850+

Plate 163

Left to right, top to bottom

Engraved silver, strap bracelet set with Scottish agates and cornelian.
£120 — £190

Crowned 'Mary Queen of Scots' heart in silver, set with bloodstone and cornelian.
£85 — £100

Shield-shaped brooch in silver, set with agates and jasper.
£90 — £130

Celtic style brooch in silver, set with agates, bloodstone and jasper.
£90 — £120

Silver-gilt bracelet with padlock fastening, set with agates.
£140 — £220

Circular open-work brooch in silver, the centre a 'cairngorm' (dark citrine), the border of various granites with foiled citrines, amethysts and garnets.
£220 — £260

Eight-lobed brooch, set with agates and cornelian, on a black slate base, in silver.
£100 — £120

Rectangular silver, agate and jasper brooch, centre silver panel engraved with an ivy motif, probably made in Birmingham.
£80 — £100

Ring brooch of agates, bloodstones, citrine, foiled citrines and amethyst in silver.
£110 — £170

Eight-lobed brooch, set with bloodstone and agates, mounted on black slate and set in silver.
£110 — £150

Scottish brooch, set with jasper and bloodstone, the engraved silver corners set with foiled cabochon amethysts.
£160 — £220

Dirk in Scottish style, marked 'SILVER', probably made in Birmingham, set with cornelian bloodstone and citrines.
£85 — £110

Scottish dirk brooch, set with cornelian, jasper, agates, bloodstone and foiled citrines in silver.
£120 — £160

(Courtesy of Antiquarius, Thesaurus)

Plate 164

Left to right, top to bottom
Bohemian garnet earrings, set in gold, c.1860.
£190 — £240
Rosette-shaped, gold earrings with drops, of classical inspiration, c.1860.
£320 — £380
Circular hollow gold earrings with applied thread decoration, c.1870.
£240 — £275
Silver-gilt, drop earrings set with almandine garnets, c.1855.
£185 — £210
Faceted cornelian, drop earrings in an oak-leaf designed mount, c.1855.
£185 — £225
A fine pair of cameo set, drop earrings in an ornate scrolled gold mount, c.1850.
£750 — £1,000
Long cornelian drop earrings, c.1860.
£190 — £240
Coral and gold urn-shaped earrings, c.1860.
£200 — £260
Gold target earrings with acorn shaped drops, applied thread decoration, c.1860.
£310 — £350
A pair of reproduction, red enamel and gold drop earrings in the mid-Victorian style.
£185 — £240

19th and 20th Century Earrings

(Cameo Corner)

(Courtesy of Antiquarius, Anne Tan, Thesaurus, The Purple Shop and Tony & Sara)

Plate 165

Left to right, top to bottom
A pair of Georgian, pinchbeck, mesh, drop earrings, c.1825.
£110 — £140
A pair of Victorian, tortoiseshell, piqué-work, double loop, drop earrings.
£175 — £250
A pair of Georgian, coral, cameo, drop earrings mounted in gold.
£150 — £210
A pair of mid-Victorian, 15ct. gold, drop earrings.
£260 — £350
A pair of mid-Victorian, coral cluster earrings with rose diamonds in gold.
£200 — £250
A pair of mid-Victorian, circular, mosaic earrings in silver-gilt, c.1860.
£80 — £120
A pair of late 19th century, Hungarian coral and pearl earrings in silver-gilt, c.1880.
£80 — £130
A pair of tiger's claws mounted in 9ct. gold as earrings, c.1880.
£75 — £100
A pair of 18ct. gold, rosette, crescent and tassel drop earrings, c.1880.
£180 — £250
A pair of anchor earrings, enamelled with pink roses on black, set in base metal.
£75 — £100

Plate 166

Left to right, top to bottom
A pair of Japanese enamel
earrings, c.1900.
£50 — £75
Silver earrings set with various
semi-precious stones, collet and
claw set, c.1940.
£90 — £110
Art deco earrings with
chalcedony drops, mounted in
silver and marcasite.
£90 — £110
Art deco, marcasite and silver,
drop earrings.
£90 — £120
Art deco, cornelian and
marcasite, drop earrings, set in
silver.
£65 — £90
Silver-gilt and enamel, Egyptian
style earrings, c.1920.
£70 — £90
Circular stud earrings, with a
centre pearl surrounded by onyx
and marcasites in silver.
£55 — £85
A pair of paste drop earrings,
set in metal, c.1925.
£50 — £60
A pair of marcasite and metal
earrings, c.1940.
£40 — £55
A pair of earrings, the drops of
real butterfly wings behind
painted glass, set and backed in
silver, c.1940.
£40 — £70

*(Courtesy of Antiquarius, Tony & Sara, Bellamy, Thesaurus, The
Purple Shop and Lynda Perkin Antiques)*

Plate 167

1. A pair of Victorian earrings, in the form of a hanging basket of flowers, in three-colour gold with pearls and tourmalines, c.1860.
   £550 — £650

2. A pair of Georgian, filigree gold and chalcedony drop earrings, c.1825.
   £450 — £600

3. A pair of mid-Victorian, drop earrings in matt gold, enamelled and set with garnets and diamonds, c.1860.
   £525 — £625

4. A pair of Victorian, urn-shaped, drop earrings in banded agate and gold, c.1850.
   £600 — £800

5. A pair of 18th century, Russian gold and pearl drop earrings, designed as large bunches of grapes.
   £650 — £750

6. A pair of mid-Victorian, banded agate (sardonyx), pearl, black enamel and gold drop earrings, c.1860.
   £600 — £700

7. A pair of art deco, fire opal and diamond, drop earrings set in platinum, c.1920.
   £1,100 — £1,350

8. A pair of 20th century, Oriental pearl and diamond earrings, the black and white pearls of large size, c.1930.
   £10,000+

9. A pair of art deco, Oriental pearl and diamond drop earrings, the pearl clusters suspended from an open diamond-set triangle, c.1935.
   £2,750 — £3,300

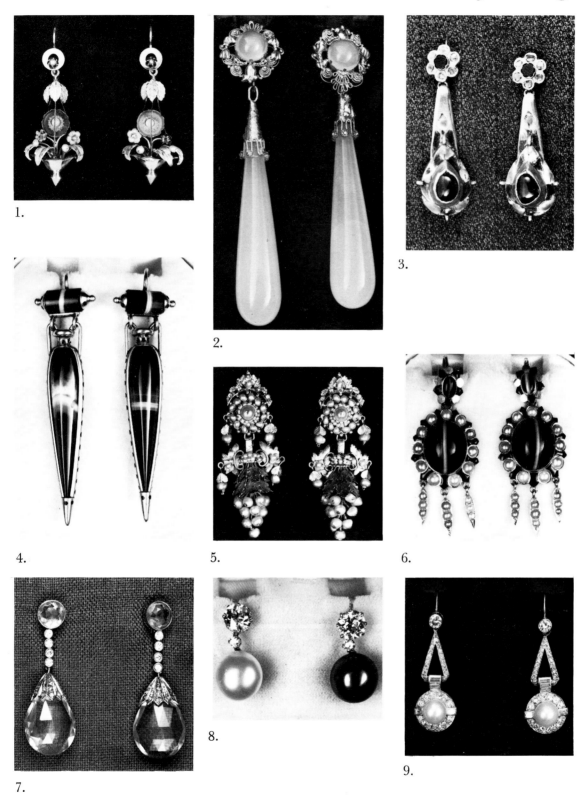

1.

2.

3.

4.

5.

6.

7.

8.

9.

(Photographs all N. Bloom except No. 7 Michael Poynder)

Plate 168

Left to right, top to bottom
Finely enamelled, butterly brooch, by Giuliano, c.1890.
£3,750 — £5,000
Blue enamel and gold floral pendant with the gold figure of a child in the centre, by
Castellani.
£1,650 — £2,200
Square mosaic brooch with gold rope border, in the Greek style, with Greek mosaic
lettering, by Castellani.
£725 — £950
Circular, hollow gold, ram's head brooch, by Castellani.
£1,550 — £2,000
Gold target brooch with a ram's head, by Giuliano (more influenced by Castellani's work
than many of his pieces).
£2,400 — £3,000
A pair of enamel and rose diamond earrings in the form of a pelican entwined with a snake,
by Giuliano.
£4,400 — £5,500
A pair of classical scarabs, mounted by Castellani in a gold setting as a brooch.
£1,850 — £2,450
Turquoise, ruby, diamond and enamel fan brooch, by Giuliano.
£1,100 — £1,450
Layered agate, blue and white enamel pendant with locket opening on reverse, by Giuliano.
£2,200 — £2,750
Classical Greek coin set in gold as a brooch, by Castellani.
£1,100 — £1,500
Carved, cabochon, amethyst brooch, set in gold, by Castellani.
£825 — £1,100
Lapis lazuli and gold bead necklace, by Giuliano.
£5,500 — £6,600
Black and white enamel pendant set with five moonstones, by Giuliano.
£1,350 — £1,750

(S.J. Phillips)

Castellani, 1793–1865

Castellani was an Italian goldsmith and jeweller, working in London, who specialised in the reproduction of Roman and Etruscan gold-work, which he discovered was still being produced by the original methods in a small village called St. Angelo, Vado, in Italy. His two sons, Alessandro and Augusto, continued and expanded his business and many of their pieces have been exhibited in museums throughout the world. Because of the excellent quality, their work is much sought after when it appears in the salerooms.

Carlo Giuliano, d. 1895

Giuliano was another Italian goldsmith, and much influenced by the work of Castellani. In the 1860s he set up shop at Frith Street, moving to 115 Piccadilly in 1875. His work concentrated more on the reproduction of Italian Renaissance jewellery rather than Roman and Etruscan designs, and he fashioned his pieces to the taste of the Victorians of the time. After his death his two sons, Frederico and Ferdinando, continued the business until it finally closed in 1914.

CG   C.& A.G.

The work of both Castellani and Giuliano is collected and the prices are therefore rising steadily.

Plate 169

Late 19th century, gold fringe necklace in the Hellenistic style, by Giuliano, c.1885. The S-link clasp is typical of Giuliano's work. The maker's mark is clearly visible on this clasp; it could be argued that the necklace might therefore be faked. However, the quality of the goldwork is such that it could not be reproduced economically today.

£5,000 — £6,000

215

Plate 170

Left to right, top to bottom

Turquoise and ruby, heart brooch of open design, set in gold, c.1875.
£2,000 — £2,200

Enamel portrait, set in a frame of green, blue, white and black enamel, and pearls, c.1890.
£2,500 — £2,750

Sapphire, diamond and pearl, spray flower brooch, c.1880, retailed by Giuliano, although not made by the firm.
£1,500 — £1,650

Rose diamond, enamel and pearl three-row necklace, Carlo and Arthur Giuliano, c.1890.
£6,000 — £6,600

Green tourmaline, cinnamon diamond, enamel and pearl pendant.
£5,000 — £6,000

Black and white enamel pendant in the form of a stylised cross, set with rubies and pearls.
£5,000 — £6,000

(Wartski)

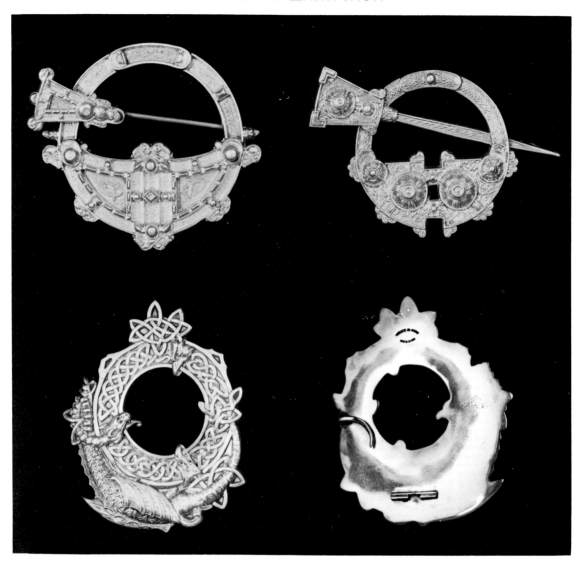

(Michael Poynder)

Plate 171

Left to right, top to bottom
Mid-Victorian, Celtic revival brooch in silver-gilt, by Waterhouse of Dublin, c.1850.
£350 — £475
Celtic Tara brooch, silver-gilt, unmarked, c.1850.
£140 — £250
Celtic style, dragon brooch, silver-gilt, by West of Dublin, dated 1871 by its British
Registry Mark.
£125 — £175
Reverse of the above, showing engraved maker's name at the top, and on the right the
British Registry Mark. (See enlargement and details with Plate 273.)

A number of these brooches were made in the mid-19th century after archaeological finds in
Ireland shortly before. The revival brooches were made in gold, silver, silver-gilt and
parcel-gilt.

(Courtesy of Antiquarius, Thesaurus and The Purple Shop)

Plate 172

Left to right, top to bottom
Late Georgian, gold vinaigrette,
c.1830.
£175 — £275
9ct. gold, engraved locket,
c.1880.
£100 — £120
15ct. gold, rose diamond and
turquoise locket in the Gothic
style, c.1865.
£220 — £300
Georgian, gold locket (shown
open)
£100 — £150
9ct. gold locket with hair-work
centre (shown open).
£100 — £150

9ct. gold heart locket set with
rubies and pearls, c.1880.
£100 — £150
18ct. gold oval locket, engraved
and with applied decoration.
£100 — £150
9ct. gold, oval, 'back and front'
locket. (The hinge and other
fittings are of metal.)
£80 — £120
Edwardian, 9ct. gold, heart
locket, engraved surface,
c.1905.
£80 — £120
9ct. gold, ruby and pearl locket,

slightly damaged on back.
£80 — £120
9ct. gold, 'back and front'
locket, c.1880.
£80 — £120
9ct. gold, engraved locket,
c.1880.
£80 — £120
9ct. gold locket with shield,
engraved and with applied decoration, c.1880.
£80 — £120
Shield shaped, 15ct. gold locket
showing classical influence,
c.1850.
£180 — £240

(Michael Poynder)

Plate 173

Left to right, top to bottom

Early Victorian, floral locket in the form of a gold heart with a matt gold finish, set with various stones, one flower spelling 'Regard', and the other, 'Dear', c.1840. The initials of various stones were used to spell out these words, e.g. 'Dear' is Diamond, Emerald, Amethyst and Ruby.

£700 — £800

Georgian, circular locket set with graduated pearls in gold, the crystal centre empty, c.1820.

£250 — £300

Georgian, 'Regard' brooch in a rectangular, gold mount, c.1835. (Illustrated in colour in Plate 198.)

£450 — £550

Early Victorian, floral gold and turquoise locket with empty glass centre, c.1845.

£375 — £475

Victorian gold and pearl locket with fine gold work, c.1855.

£350 — £450

Early Victorian, pavé set turquoise heart locket in silver-gilt, c.1845.

£200 — £250

220

Plate 174

Left to right, top to bottom

Oval, gold locket containing the original photographs, c.1885.
£280 — £360

Pale blue enamel and gold locket, set with pearls, c.1870.
£300 — £340

Oval, gold locket with applied thread decoration, the centre of turquoise enamel and set with a pearl, c.1875.
£350 — £390

Floral, gold locket set with an amethyst, pearls and rose diamonds, c.1880.
£1,800 — £2,200

Oval, 15ct. gold locket with diagonal band of applied decoration, c.1860.
£350 — £380

Oval, gold locket of fine quality, with a diamond set flower, on a hollow large link chain, c.1875.
£1,700 — £2,400

Oval, 15ct. gold locket with a vertical band of *repoussé* decoration, c.1860.
£250 — £300

(Cameo Corner)

221

19th Century Hungarian Enamel Jewellery

(Courtesy of Antiquarius, Catherine Derry, The Purple Shop, Tony & Sara and Thesaurus)

Plate 175

Left to right, top to bottom
Pendant of St. George and the Dragon, enamelled and set with garnets and pearls.
£230 — £310
Silver-gilt and enamelled butterfly set with turquoises and garnets.
£100 — £125
A pair of enamel and silver-gilt, rosette earrings, originally part of necklace, set with pearls and coral.
£95 — £130
Pearl, turquoise and garnet, floral pendant set in silver-gilt.
£50 — £80
Hungarian, St. George and the Dragon, pendant, enamelled and set with a baroque drop pearl.
£110 — £180
Turquoise and pearl brooch, in scrolled silver-gilt mount, c.1835.
£100 — £130
Late 19th century, silver-gilt, garnet, turquoise and pearl oval pendant.
£100 — £150
Enamelled silver frame on a chain, set with rubies, a diamond and an aquamarine.
£250 — £320

Plate 176

19th century Hungarian pendant in the 17th century style, the frame of enamelled silver, set with pearls and rubies, the centre of a cornelian and glass doublet cameo. The spotted appearance of the cameo is a layer of air bubbles trapped between the glass and the cornelian where the glue with which they were stuck together has deteriorated.
£650 — £900

(Thesaurus at Antiquarius)

Plate 177

Left to right, top to bottom
Mid-Victorian, green enamel and rose diamond, target brooch, c.1860.
£520 — £600
Flesh-coloured enamel, snail brooch with diamond body, set in white gold, by Boucheron, modern.
£850 — £1,050
Mid-19th century, Limoges enamel, profile head in a ruby and diamond star-shaped frame, set in gold, c.1870.
£850 — £1,000
Mid-19th century, Limoges enamel circular brooch with a pearl frame, c.1860.
£600 — £700
Edwardian, pink enamel and pearl pendant on chain, c.1905.
£500 — £600
Mid-Victorian, oval brooch with a painted enamel scene of a nymph with two fauns, in a ruby and diamond frame, c.1850.
£750 — £1,050
Mid-19th century, Swiss, enamel brooch in a rectangular gold frame, c.1850.
£650 — £900
Mid-19th century, Swiss, enamel brooch of 'The Adoration of the Magi', c.1850.
£650 — £900

(N. Bloom)

Plate 178

Left to right, top to bottom
Late Victorian, diamond swallow brooch, set in silver and gold, c.1880.
£850 — £1,200
19th century, 18ct. gold, ruby and diamond stork brooch, French, c.1860.
£950 — £1,300
Diamond, emerald and ruby set falcon, standing on a group of baroque pearls.
£750 — £950
Sapphire, diamond and pearl butterfly brooch, the platinum body made as a spring to allow
movement of the wings.
£1,800 — £2,300
Diamond butterfly brooch, set with white, yellow and cinnamon-coloured diamonds.
£5,000 — £7,000
Victorian butterfly brooch, the mother-of-pearl body set with green garnets and rubies in
gold, c.1890.
£750 — £850
Victorian fly brooch, set with pearls, rubies and rose diamonds in yellow gold, c.1860.
£850 — £1,200
Victorian lizard brooch, set with diamonds and green garnets, with ruby eyes, c.1880.
£1,600 — £2,200
Victorian, diamond butterfly brooch, with ruby eyes and a gold body, c.1880.
£950 — £1,350

(N. Bloom)

Plate 179

Left to right, top to bottom
Silver bird, c.1880.
Target brooch with applied decoration. c.1875.
Target brooch, c.1880.
Silver and gold shamrock brooch, c.1880.
Silver and gold 'Le Havre' brooch, c.1915.
Silver name brooch, 'Beatie', c.1870.
Two love birds, c.1890.
Silver and pearl, open-work brooch, 'Annie', c.1880.
Shoe, c.1880.
Silver name brooch, 'Eliza', c.1890.
Silver 'Baby' brooch, c.1880.
Silver and two-colour gold brooch set with an agate, c.1885.
Silver 'Baby' nappy pin, c.1880.
Silver Jubilee brooch, 1887.
Late 19th century 'Japanese' fans.
Silver dog brooch, 'Pet', c.1900.
Silver anchor and enamelled bird brooch, c.1875.
Die-cast silver cockerel.
French, British, Belgian and Dutch flag brooch, enamelled on metal, c.1914.
Double flag brooch, enamelled, c.1914.
Single flag brooch, c.1914.
£25 — £65 each

(Courtesy of Antiquarius, The Purple Shop, Thesaurus and Tony & Sara)

Amulets and Talismans

Since man first knew fear and learnt to kill, he has worn "bits and pieces" to give him courage to face the dangers of life, both mystical and practical. These "things" are known as amulets or talismans and take many forms — the claws of a slain animal, the neck bone of a tiger, the hair from an elephant's tail, a piece of coral (particularly thought to ward off disease), or a pure crystal as a protection against pests. Magical qualities have been given to many different stones, and hence the development of the zodiacal birth stone charts in the Appendix. Animals, in whom man identifies so many of his own characteristics, are supposed to have special attributes; the Egyptians used the fish as a love symbol. Foxes, spiders, ladybirds and even pigs are thought to be lucky in various parts of the world; bats are a symbol of longevity, health and peace to the Chinese. Horse shoes, and anything crescent shaped has a long tradition of magic and good luck and was used as a protection against witches and the plague — hence nailing a shoe to your cottage door. The cross is perhaps the greatest symbolic talisman we wear in the West, for obvious reasons, and medieval confidence tricksters sold pieces of the "true cross" and bones of the martyrs centuries after the death of Christ to bring the wearer protection from the devil.

The necklace of stones and nuts was gathered no doubt by a pilgrim, probably a Buddhist or Trappist monk during a pilgrimage and set to mark attainment of that goal.

Plate 180

Left to right, top to bottom
Early 19th century lady's shoe, made of jasper.
£15 — £20
Late 19th century, metal hobnail boot.
£15 — £20
Edwardian 'Alpha and Omega' pendant, set with rose diamonds in white gold, c.1910.
£160 — £200
14ct. gold and enamel lady-bird pendant, modern.
£65 — £90
Mid-19th century, Italian mosaic, 'Pax' pendant.
£50 — £80
Early 18th century, flat-cut garnet and gold witch's heart brooch.
£90 — £140
Victorian, 9ct. gold whistle.
£90 — £130
Late Victorian, silver and coloured glass, bee brooch, c.1880.
£120 — £150
Nepalese, silver, female monkey god, traditional, 20th century.
£30 — £40
Thai, composition stone god, set in silver.
£20 — £25
Early 19th century, Chinese carved cornelian 'peach of longevity'.
£60 — £90

(Courtesy of Antiquarius, The Purple Shop, Thesaurus and Stall M1)

Nepalese silver monkey god, traditional, probably late 19th century.
£30 — £40
Thai stone god in silver, traditional, probably 20th century.
£30 — £40
Afghani Koran medal, made in low-grade silver, traditional.
£35 — £45
Tibetan, double tooth pendant, silver-mounted.
£30 — £40
Victorian, silver-gilt, mounted otter pad, c.1885.
£35 — £50

(*Antiquarius, Stall M1*)

Plate 181

A Coptic Jimma Jala, traditionally made in the same way as the early Christian silver necklaces, with each section of silver containing charcoal, which the wearers believed to be health-giving.
£250 — £350
Traditional Coptic Cross, in silver.
£30 — £50
Coptic, leather prayer-holder.
£30 — £50
Coptic, silver ear-pick.
£50 — £60

Plate 182

Left to right, top to bottom
Red and yellow 18ct. gold ring with applied gold hearts and star.
£75 — £90
Three stone, diamond, gypsy-set ring with engraved gold band, c.1890.
£120 — £150
Five stone, diamond ring, the stones set into an elongated hexagonal section, c.1900.
£140 — £190
Ruby and diamond, three stone, gypsy-set ring in 18ct. gold, c.1890.
£170 — £275
Ruby and pearl, double banded, half-hoop ring in 18ct. yellow gold, c.1900.
£140 — £180
Sapphire and diamond, five stone, gypsy-set ring in 18ct. yellow gold, c.1885.
£140 — £180
22ct. gold buckle ring, set with two rose diamonds.
£140 — £180
Coral and two turquoises set as a three stone ring in a wide gold band.
£150 — £200
Three stone, coral ring in a wide 18ct. gold band.
£150 — £180
18ct. gold, buckle ring set with diamonds and sapphires.
£260 — £320
Sapphire, ruby and pearl diagonally set ring in 15ct. gold.
£150 — £180

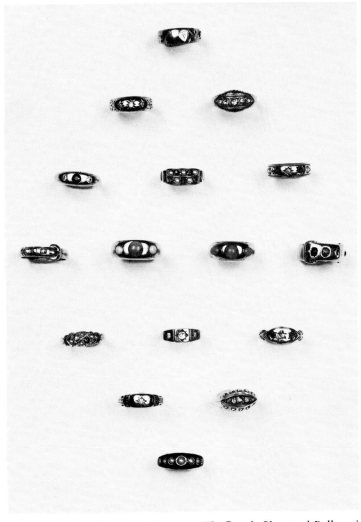

(Courtesy of Antiquarius, Thesaurus, The Purple Shop and Bellamy)

Three stone, diamond, gypsy-set ring, c.1890.
£150 — £180
Ruby and diamond, three stone gypsy-set ring in a boat-shaped gold mount.
£150 — £180
Single diamond, gypsy-set in a gold ring.
£120 — £150

Ruby and diamond, graduated five stone ring in an ornate gold mount, c.1895.
£125 — £155
Black enamel ring set with seven pearls in silver.
£130 — £160

(Antiquarius, Stall M1)

Plate 183

Left to right, top to bottom
Algerian, enamelled silver pendant, on a hand-moulded resin bead and carved coral necklace.
£160 — £275
Coral necklace with silver bead pendants, from Goa, S.W. India.
£210 — £320
Coral necklace, with two silver discs and a central silver bead, from N. Africa.
£320 — £420
Small coral and silver bead necklace, with silver pendant inlaid with gutta percha, from N. Africa.
£150 — £200
Indian, graduated coral, bead necklace with a large central bead of paler coral from China.
£200 — £250
Coral bead necklace with three pieces of turquoise matrix. Tibetan.
£250 — £350
N. African, coral necklace with four silver ornamental discs.
£180 — £260

Plate 184

Top to bottom
Long string of coral beads, 48in. (120cm.) *£120 — £150*
A string of green-stained alabaster beads. *£35 — £55*
Carved amethyst and rock-crystal beads. *£275 — £350*
A string of variegated agate beads. *£120 — £150*
Graduated ivory beads. *£100 — £140*
Tiger's eye beads. *£60 — £120*
Pink coral and seed-pearl necklace. *£150 — £175*
Aventurine quartz beads. *£50 — £90*
Faceted citrine and crystal bead necklace, 24ins. (60cm) long. *£250 — £350*
Moonstone beads. *£120 — £160*
A string of alternating malachite and lapis lazuli beads. *£375 — £475*
A string of faceted rose quartz beads. *£250 — £300*
Graduated sardonyx beads, 36ins. (90cm) long. *£200 — £250*
A string of blue-stained quartz beads. *£50 — £70*

(Courtesy of Antiquarius, Thesaurus, Tony & Sara, Bellamy and The Purple Shop)

Tibetan Jewellery

Plate 185

Amulet necklace, made up from pieces found on pilgrimage, beads, claws, stones, berries, nuts, coins, shells, etc., 20th century.
£300 — £400
Bead and turquoise matrix necklace.
£120 — £150
Low-grade silver prayer box, inlaid with turquoise matrix and glass, stuck in with gutta percha (a natural glutinous resin).
£120 — £150
Late 19th century skull made from a monkey femur. Earlier ones would probably be made from human skull-bone and can be expensive because of their rarity.
£90 — £120
A Mahla (rosary), made from seeds and cornelian beads, with low-grade silver counting beads, prayer bell and dorje (sacred symbol) forming pendants.
£200 — £250

(Antiquarius, Stall M1)

(Courtesy of Antiquarius, Thesaurus and Tony & Sara)

Plate 186

Left to right, top to bottom
19th century, Florentine brooch, set with various hardstones in a rectangular silver mount.
£100 — £150
Circular, floral brooch in a granulated silver-gilt mount.
£65 — £90
Oval, floral brooch in a silver mount (damaged, but would normally be priced at more).
£60 — £80
Oval ring in a 9ct. gold mount.
£90 — £120
Elongated, oval, floral spray brooch mounted in a plain silver collet.
£90 — £120
A pair of earrings in 15ct. gold.
£270 — £350
Bracelet of seven plaques, mounted in silver (slightly chipped), would normally be worth more.
£150 — £200

Jet

Jet is an intense opaque black substance, closely allied to coal in that it is a form of fossilised wood, and very light in weight.

It became popular in the Victorian era, particularly after the death of Prince Albert in 1861 when Queen Victoria went into life-long mourning. Victorian sentimentality, and an obsession with death, prescribed new forms of etiquette which lasted past the turn of the century. Mourning cards and letters of sympathy were written on black-edged paper, in black ink, and widows wore the veil and attendant black jewellery as a mark of respect.

Jet was the obvious mineral to be used for this form of jewellery, as there was an abundant supply found in Yorkshire, near Whitby. Yet demand was such that during the height of its popularity jet was even imported from Spain. Many factories were turning out beads, crosses, earrings, brooches and pendants, as can be seen in the illustrations. Jet carving also became a cottage industry, with many little, front-room windows acting as selling space at Whitby. A high degree of carving was obtained because of the comparative ease of cutting.

Technicalities: Composition: fossilised wood. Hardness: 2½. S.G.: 1.30-1.35 (not very dense). R.I.: 1.66. Jet has been imitated by moulded glass which is commonly known as "French jet" or "Vauxhall glass" and the beautiful comb in Plate 189 is an example of this. It is reasonably easy to detect the difference between real jet and French jet, as the back of French jet has a texture rather like the skin of an orange, showing the bubbles found in moulded glass. Vauxhall glass was always mounted on japanned black metal plates. Black onyx, a form of agate, is often confused with jet and was used extensively in the 1920s and 1930s. It was at this time that black Bakelite was used to simulate jet in the same way that white Bakelite simulated ivory. The normal test for jet is to touch it with a heated needle when it will burn with a smell similar to coal. Glass and agate will not respond, and Bakelite will give off a smell of burning plastic.

Plate 187

Left to right, top to bottom
Jet bangle, each section threaded on elasticated silk.
Jet cameo brooch.
Mid-Victorian, funereal jet earrings, c.1850.
Jet drop earrings set with shell cameos, c.1855.
Jet necklace with floral engraved pendant, of Oriental influence, c.1885.
Carved jet cross with silver pendant attachment.
Jet cross.
£65 — £250 all items

(Cameo Corner)

(Courtesy of Antiquarius, Tony & Sara, Thesaurus)

Plate 188

Left to right, top to bottom
Jet necklace with locket pendant (damaged, in good condition would be worth more).
A pair of jet, drop earrings with shell cameos inset.
Jet necklace with tassel-shaped drops, c.1850.
A pair of open, loop-shaped, jet, drop earrings.
A pair of jet earrings, the metal-backed bows suspending tassel-shaped drops, c.1850.
Jet bracelet on elasticated thread with carved, oval, rose centre.
Victorian carved jet, cameo brooch.
A string of carved, jet beads.
£60 — £250 all items

(Richard Digby)

Plate 189

Mid-19th century, French jet and tortoiseshell comb. The lustre is
stronger and glassier than real jet.
£150 — £250
Victorian, gold hat pin with applied gold-work decoration.
£120 — £140
Victorian, turquoise matrix and gold hat pin.
£100 — £120
Cabochon amethyst and gold veil pin.
£100 — £120
Peridot and pearl cluster, veil pin.
£120 — £150
An assortment of five Victorian stickpins for cravats.
£50 — £75 each
Victorian, gold hat pin with applied gold decoration.
£100 — £120
Art nouveau, turquoise, matrix and gold hat pin.
£120

Chinese Jade

Plate 190

Left to right, top to bottom
Pale green jade bangle.
£100 — £200
Spinach-green jade (nephrite)
bangle.
£80 — £120
Ancient, jade, funeral bangle.
£250 — £500
Bowentie bangle (an imitation
of jade) with silver repair
bands.
£120 — £150
Pale green jade ring.
£85 — £100
Dark green jade (nephrite)
ring.
£75 — £90
Floral, carved jade (jadeite)
ring, set in gold.
£120 — £150
Jade archer's thumb-ring.
£120 — £150
Rose quartz, floral carving.
£100 — £120
Jade pendant with Indian
inscription.
£100 — £130
Dark green jade, archer's
ring.
£120 — £180
Jade bead necklace with
variegated coloured beads.
£200 — £350

(Courtesy of Antiquarius, Stall M1, Thesaurus, The Purple Shop and Tony & Sara)

Modern, open-work, carved steatite pendant, imitating brownish and pale green jade. Steatite is better known as soapstone because of its soapy, greasy feeling, and is soft enough to be scratched with a finger nail whereas jade is much harder.
£25 — £50
Cylindrical jade bead on a silver chain, as a necklace.
£200 — £250
Carved steatite pendant.
£25 — £45

Victorian and Second-Hand Chains

(Thesaurus at Antiquarius)

Plate 191

Left to right
Victorian, silver-gilt mesh link chain, 60ins. (144cm) long.
£175 — £190
Three-colour gold watch-chain, with powder flask.
£220 — £280
Mid-Victorian, silver watch-chain.
£85 — £120
9ct. gold, snake link chain, 24ins. (57.6cm) long.
£95 — £135
9ct. gold, disc link chain, 26ins. (62.4cm) long.
£110 — £160
Victorian, 9ct. gold, curb chain, 60ins. (144cm) long.
£250 — £350
Mid-Victorian, silver watch-chain.
£75 — £100
9ct. gold watch-chain.
£180 — £250
Silver-gilt, flat mesh, link chain, 30ins. (72cm) long.
£110 — £150
Silver and gold watch-chain with medallion.
£110 — £150

Plate 192

Left to right
9ct. gold, curb chain, 20ins.
(48cm) long.
£180 — £260
9ct. gold, treble trace chain,
16ins. (38.4cm) long.
£70 — £95
9ct. gold, open snake link
chain, 42ins. (100.8cm) long.
£420 — £500
9ct. gold, decorative link
chain, 17ins. (40.8cm) long.
£90 — £100
9ct. gold, snake link chain,
22ins. (52.8cm) long.
£120 — £160
9ct. gold, fine curb chain,
26ins. (62.4cm) long.
£100 — £130
9ct. gold, decorative link
chain, 14ins. (33.6cm) long.
£100 — £130
9ct. red and white gold,
decorative link chain, 14ins.
(33.6cm) long.
£120 — £140
9ct. gold, decorative link
chain, 14ins. (33.6cm) long.
£120 — £150
9ct. gold, guard chain, 46ins.
(110.4cm) long.
£400 — £500
9ct. gold, guard chain, 36ins.
(86.4cm) long.
£350 — £400

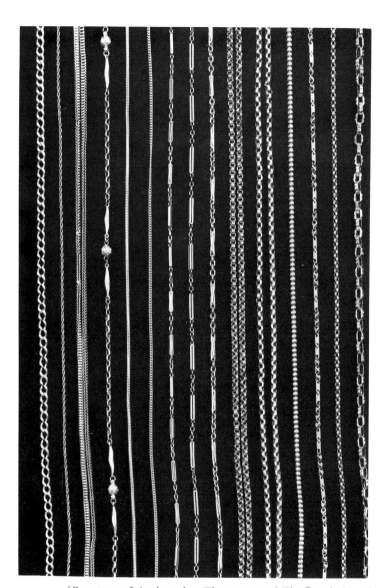

(Courtesy of Antiquarius, Thesaurus and The Purple Shop)

9ct. gold, decorative link chain, 16ins. (38.4cm) long.
£110 — £130
9ct. red and white gold, decorative link chain, 16ins. (38.4cm) long.
£120 — £150
9ct. decorative gold, guard chain, 26ins. (62.4cm) long.
£120 — £150
9ct. gold, decorative, open link chain, 15ins. (36cm) long.
£140 — £170

242

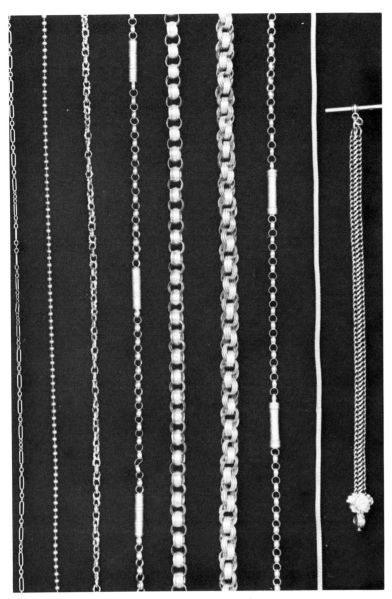

Plate 193

Left to right
9ct. white gold, long link chain,
32ins. (76.8cm) long.
£260 — £300
Victorian, 9ct. gold, ball chain,
19ins. (45.6cm) long.
£220 — £270
18ct. gold, textured link chain,
30ins. (72cm) long.
£1,200 — £1,600
18ct. gold, barrel and open link
chain, 1.1ozs., 35ins., (84cm)
long.
£900 — £1,200
18ct. gold, muff chain, 2.7ozs.,
33ins. (79.2cm) long.
£1,700 — £2,100
18ct. gold, double link chain
3.05ozs., 26ins. (62.4cm) long.
£2,000 — £2,500
18ct. gold, barrel and open link
chain, 37ins. (88.8cm) long.
£900 — £1,000
18ct. gold long, hand-woven
mesh chain, 57ins. (136.8cm)
long.
£1,000 — £1,500
18ct. gold, fob chain, by
McIntosh & McCulloch,
Glasgow c.1850, 9½ins.
(22.8cm) long.
£500 — £600

(N. Bloom)

Amber

Amber is yellow, brown or red in colour and is a fossilised pine resin. Sometimes it includes natural insects and when found as such it is considered to be a talisman.

It dates from before the Ice Age and most deposits are thought to be some 30,000,000 years old. It is soft, light, and preferably clear and can be polished and carved although it is not normally faceted in jewellery. As stated, it can include flies, beetles, fish-scales and sometimes vegetable seeds, and was thought to have magical properties in ancient times because it conducts electricity. Amber has long been popular in jewellery form, and more recently the Victorians made use of it extensively. Long strings of beads were worn by aesthetic ladies in the art nouveau and art deco periods. Since large pieces of amber are comparatively rare, a process was developed whereby small pieces were pressed together to form a substance called ambroid. It is relatively easy to distinguish, as the pieces were fused together under heat and pressure, and it is possible to see clear fusion lines.

The main source is the Baltic coast of Russia where it is obtained from shallow mines, and red amber is washed up on the shore and out of the sand. Amber also comes from Burma, Italy, and the Black Sea. It is normally cut with a smooth polished surface as beads, rings, brooches or pendants, which are sometimes carved.

Technicalities: Hardness: about 2. S.G.: 1.08. R.I.: 1.54. Amber is often imitated, particularly by Bakelite and celluloid, and more recently by polystyrene. Glass has also been used in imitation, but this is much heavier and harder. The best test for amber is to cut a minute portion away from as inconspicuous a place as possible (perhaps round a mounted ring, or from under a claw) and to place the chip in a flame. True amber will burn with a pleasant smell, whereas Bakelite will char, celluloid will flare and polystyrene will smell foul.

Plate 194

Left to right, top to bottom
A string of oval, red plastic, translucent beads, simulating amber. *£30 — £35*
A good string of graduated, oval, orange amber beads. *£150 — £180*
Pale, sea-amber, bead necklace. *£90 — £130*
Lozenge-shaped pendant of pressed amber, with black silk tassel. (It is possible to see the lines on the surface of the pendant where individual small pieces of amber have been fused or 'pressed' together under heat.) *£50 — £70*
Georgian, translucent, carved amber brooch in the form of a daisy. *£75 — £100*
Yellow amber ring, set in silver. *£25 — £35*
Circular, amber bead brooch. *£30 — £40*
Large yellow/orange amber pendant. *£80 — £120*
Art deco, transparent amber and silver ring. *£45 — £65*
Small amber bead necklace, the centre plaque with a ship engraved on the underside of the circular section, allowing the motif to show through the surface of the amber. *£70 — £100*
Modern amber ring, carved from one piece of amber. *£70 — £90*
Art deco, yellow amber and silver brooch. *£40 — £50*
Late Victorian, faceted amber circular brooch. *£30 — £40*
A string of translucent, red/orange, faceted amber beads. *£175 — £275*
A choker formed of cylindrical amber beads of varying colours. *£100 — £120*

(Courtesy of Antiquarius, Thesaurus, Tony & Sara, The Purple Shop and Bellamy)

Plate 195

Left to right, top to bottom
20th century, green jade and gold circular pendant in the form of a 'pi', made in China for the export market.
£550 — £650
19th century, spinach-green, carved jade pendant.
£450 — £550
20th century, carved cornelian, enamel and pearl brooch, c.1920.
£350 — £400
Japanese, circular bronze brooch, the surface applied with quails and peonies in gold and silver.
£80 — £130
Late 19th century, Japanese, Satsuma buckle, enamelled and gilded pottery.
£100 — £125
Late 19th century, Japanese, Satsuma enamelled circular pendant.
£125 — £150
Art deco, jade drop pendant.
£150 — £280
Late Victorian, double tiger's claw brooch, set in an engraved silver mount.
£100 — £130
Late Victorian, double tiger's claw brooch, in a floral gold mount, c.1880. Tiger's claw jewellery was very popular soon after Queen Victoria became Empress of India in 1876.
£170 — £220

Late 19th & 20th Century Jade, Japanese Enamel, and Ivory

(N. Bloom)

(N. Bloom)

(N. Bloom)

(Thesaurus at Antiquarius)

(Thesaurus at Antiquarius)

(Thesaurus at Antiquarius)

(Thesaurus at Antiquarius)

(Thesaurus at Antiquarius)

(Thesaurus at Antiquarius)

Plate 196

Left to right, top to bottom
A pair of star rubies, set as cufflinks surrounded by baguette diamonds in platinum,
approximately 14cts. rubies.
£150,000 — £250,000

A fine star ruby of good colour and showing pronounced asterism, weighing 26.66cts. This
is a particularly good colour for a star stone as the background colour is normally much
milkier. Although the asterism is said to be pronounced, it does not show in the photograph
as well as the cufflinks above.
£750,000 — £1,000,000

A pair of star ruby and diamond cluster earrings, weight of the two rubies approximately
22cts., and a cabochon ruby and diamond cluster ring, the ruby weighing approximately
15cts.
£50,000 — £80,000

(Sotheby Parke Bernet, Hong Kong)

Cuff Links and Stick Pins

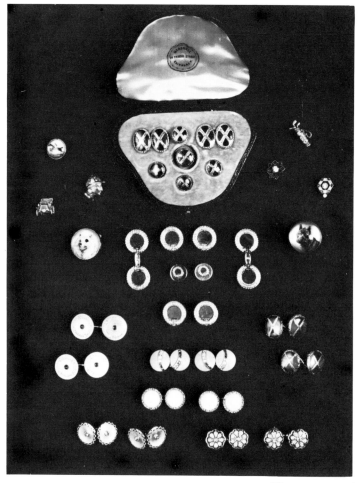

(Harvey & Gore)

Plate 197

A set of Scottish, pebble agate cufflinks and studs set in engraved gold, c.1880.
£650 — £750
Essex crystal, race-horse stick-pin.
£190 — £225
Carved moonstone, jockey's head stick-pin with diamonds and blue enamel in gold, c.1900.
£325 — £375
Gold, vintage car stick-pin set with a diamond.
£200 — £250

Essex crystal, Pomeranian stick-pin.
£225 — £250
Bag of golf-clubs, set with diamonds and green garnets, as a stick-pin.
£350 — £390
Octagonal diamond and emerald stick-pin in gold mount.
£300 — £400
Art deco ruby and diamond stick-pin set in platinum.
£250 — £300
Essex crystal, Cairn stick-pin.
£225 — £275
A set of lapis lazuli and diamond cufflinks and studs, c.1940.
£1,500 — £2,500
A pair of cabochon emerald, diamond and engraved platinum cufflinks, c.1925.
£750 — £1,000
A pair of art deco, sapphire, diamond and platinum cufflinks, with a matt surface, c.1935.
£1,000 — £1,200
Scottish pebble cufflinks set in cross-banded gold mount, c.1880.
£250 — £375
Victorian, white agate and diamond cufflinks, c.1870.
£300 — £500
Edwardian, mother-of-pearl, diamond, gold and enamel cuff-links, c.1910.
£300 — £375
A pair of diamond and enamel cufflinks of floral design, c.1925.
£850 — £1,000

Love Jewellery

The most usual form of "love jewellery" is obviously the ring given on marriage and often suitably engraved inside. Gem set rings were expensive luxuries until comparatively recent times, as it was not until the 18th century and the opening up of trade withe Middle East and Asia that the flow of gemstones appeared on the European market. Lover's knots (the "Staffordshire knot") and hearts were usual forms of brooches either in silver, gold or stones.

French was the smart, aristocratic language of Regency England and many jewels were given bearing such delightful designs, often in precious stones as "Souvenir d'amitié", "Souvenir d'amour", "Regard" and "Dearest". These can be spelt out in coloured stones as was done with rings and pins until about 1850, and often included a lock of hair or a painted miniature of the giver. However, the severity and piousness of Victoria's reign soon stopped this sentimentality and memorial love jewellery superseded romantic love jewellery. Various plants (which were considered lucky) started to be used in design forms — acorns, holly, ivy, four-leaf clover, mistletoe and heather all appeared in silver and gold jewellery form, often set with precious or semi-precious stones.

A very popular trait between parting lovers, particularly soldiers going off to fight in campaigns in far off parts of the Empire, was the giving of "Mizpah" rings. This name is taken from a quotation in Genesis which reads: "The Lord watcheth between me and thee when we are parted one from the other."

Key and heart lockets were obvious mementoes between lovers — the key to unlock the heart and suitably engraved. Women gave their men gold or silver lockets containing hair or portraits, in the shape of small pocket watches, probably because Victorian men didn't like to show their sentimentality. The shyness and coy attitude of Victorian women towards birth is manifest in naïve little brooches, in silver and gold, showing chickens emerging from eggs and love birds on branches.

Plate 198

Left-hand side, centre top to bottom, right-hand side

Georgian, crowned paste, witch's heart, set in silver, c.1810. *£150 — £200*

Late 18th century, almandine, garnet and gold, witch's heart, set in gold. *£220 — £300*

Late 18th century, rose diamond set witch's heart. *£300 — £375*

Victorian, Staffordshire lover's knot in blue paste, pearls and gold, c.1840. *£200 — £225*

Early 19th century, rose diamond, heart pendant with moonstone centre. *£320 — £375*

Victorian, red enamel and seed pearl, link brooch, with pearl pendant heart, c.1850.
£400 — £475

Early 19th century, rose diamond set, swallow brooch, with ruby collar and eye.
£550 — £650

Late 18th century, diamond witch's heart, set in silver and gold. *£650 — £1,000*

Late Georgian, 'Regard' brooch, with a rectangular gold setting, c.1835. The stones are
Ruby, **E**merald, **G**arnet, **A**methyst, **R**uby and **D**iamond. *£450 — £550*

Late Georgian, granulated gold, turquoise and ruby heart pendant, c.1825. *£320 — £380*

Late Georgian, memorial 'Regard' brooch in gold with plaited hair centre, c.1830.
£350 — £450

Mid-Victorian, double pearl and diamond heart, in a green and white enamel single heart,
surrounded by pearls, c.1860. *£550 — £600*

Mid-Victorian, pavé set, turquoise and pearl heart on a gold chain with a turquoise and pearl
cluster,, c.1865. *£600 — £700*

Victorian, double heart brooch, set with an amethyst and a citrine, surrounded by diamonds
and crowned with a bow, c.1870. *£600 — £800*

Victorian, ruby and diamond, heart-shaped, cluster ring set in gold. *£750 — £950*

18th century, 'Fede' ring, gold hands holding a garnet. *£300 — £350*

Edwardian, blue enamel, heart-shaped ring, set with a freshwater pearl. *£350 — £450*

Reproduction 'Regard' ring in 9ct. yellow gold. *£140 — £200*

Early Victorian, 'Regard' ring in gold, c.1840. *£220 — £275*

Early Victorian, pavé set, diamond, heart brooch, set in silver and gold, c.1880.
£1,600 — £1,900

Late Victorian, double opal heart in a knot of ribbons, diamonds, set in silver and gold,
c.1880.
£1,400 — £1,600

Victorian, turquoise and diamond, miniature heart brooch. *£475 — £575*

Late 19th century, gold bar pin with interlocking crowned hearts. *£260 — £300*

Georgian, pavé set, rose diamond, pendant heart. *£500 — £600*

Late Georgian, filigree gold, 'Regard' brooch with turquoise-set flower. *£400 — £500*

Textured gold, pendant heart. *£275 — £325*

Mid-19th century, pavé set, diamond, pendant heart. *£1,500 — £1,800*

Late 18th century, crystal, heart pendant with garnet crown. *£280 — £350*

Victorian, double heart pendant of opals surrounded with diamonds, with a ribbon bow and
opal and diamond drop. *£950 — £1,400*

Mid-19th century, dark blue opal and seed pearl pendant, a heart padlock, with gold key
attached. *£350 — £450*

(Photograph copyright Vogue Magazine)

(Courtesy of Michael Poynder and Richard Ogden)

FORGET
ME
NOT

The Arts & Crafts Movement: 1880-1935

In England during the second half of the 19th century traditional jewellery continued to be made as usual. However, a new style was developing in parallel under the influence and sentiments of the Pre-Raphaelite artists, and, later, the designer William Morris. This style was developed to counter stiff, factory-made objects which, although often of excellent quality, were unimaginative and dull. Small groups of designer craftsmen formed themselves into individual guilds around the country and started producing colourful, hand-made articles in inexpensive materials, using naturalistic forms and lines, hoping to influence the public taste. These guilds became known as the "Arts and Crafts Movement" which to continue in changing form until the 1930s, encompassing the styles known in turn as "art nouveau" and "art decorative". Some of the members were emancipated women, and many jewellers and silversmiths who were associated with the movement are now well-known names as designers of imagination and talent: Ashbee, J.P. Cooper, Fisher, Gaskin, A.H. Jones, the MacDonald sisters, C.R. Mackintosh, William Morris, Omar Ramsden, Henry Wilson — to mention a few.

In jewellery the use of precious stones set in gold was largely ignored for colourful, cheaper stones in silver, often combined with the use of different enamelling techniques — *cloisonné, champlevé* and *plique-à-jour*. Several established retail businesses contracted work from individual jewellers and even mass-produced some of their designs under the firm's name, notably Liberty & Co., in England, and Tiffany in the States. This was a fascinating period of design and craftsmanship and many original and beautiful pieces of jewellery were made. For further information read Charlotte Gere's book *Victorian Jewellery Design* published by William Kimber.

(The Purple Shop Private Collection)

Plate 199

All by Wilson & Cooper, late 19th century
Top to bottom
Fire opal and silver pendant.
£250 — £300
Moonstone, opal and silver pendant on a silver chain.
£400 — £450
An agate and cornelian necklace, set in silver.
£500 — £600

Plate 200

Silver and opal rectangular brooch, arts and crafts, by Mr. and Mrs. Arthur Gaskin.
£300 — £400
Emerald, opal, tourmaline and enamel pendant on a silver chain, by Mr. and Mrs. Arthur Gaskin.
£750 — £900
Enamel and silver pendant with three drops, on a silver chain, by Omar Ramsden, unmarked. (Omar Ramsden is better known as a silversmith.)
£700 — £850

(Antiquarius, The Purple Shop)

256

Plate 201

A lapis lazuli and silver necklace, the long chain threaded with lapis lazuli beads.
£400 — £500

Plate 202

Arts and crafts, amethyst and moonstone pendant of three large clusters, set in silver,
possibly by Sybil Dunlop.
£475 — £575
Late arts and crafts turquoise matrix and silver chain necklace.
£200 — £300
We have photographed the reverse of both pieces of jewellery to show the methods of
setting.

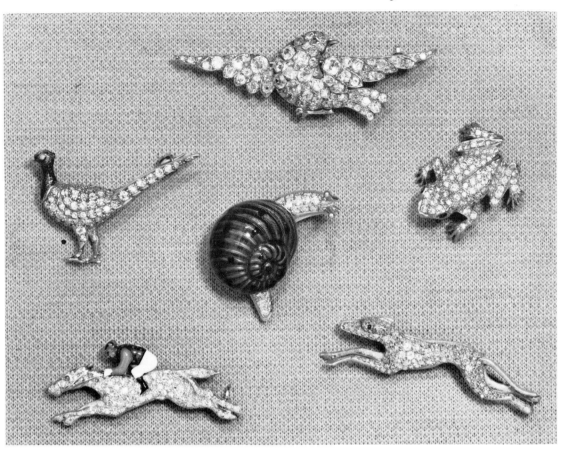

(Tessiers)

Plate 203

Pavé set diamond bird in flight, set in silver and gold.
£2,500 — £3,000
Pavé set diamond, pheasant brooch with enamelled head, set in yellow and white gold.
£1,000 — £1,400
Diamond snail with blue enamelled shell, set in yellow gold.
£1,400 — £1,600
Pavé set diamond, frog brooch set in yellow gold.
£1,000 — £1,500
Pavé set diamond race-horse with enamelled jockey, set in yellow gold.
£1,500 — £2,000
Pavé set diamond, greyhound brooch, set in yellow and white gold.
£900 — £1,100

The House of Fabergé

GUSTAV FABERGE 1814-1881
PETER CARL FABERGE 1846-1920

The Fabergé family owned a manufacturing and retail jewellery business started in St. Petersburg in 1842 by Gustav Fabergé. They were goldsmiths to the Czars and the Russian nobility, who with their immense wealth gave them full rein to produce magnificent and extravagant examples of the goldsmith's and enameller's art, probably unrivalled since the days of Cellini. Fabergé and his craftsmen are renowned for their "objets d'art" and "objets de vertu", which include Easter eggs, dinner services, and in particular, hardstone animals and flowers. They also produced many of the flamboyant, jewelled Orders of the time. Surprisingly enough they seemed to neglect small pieces of jewellery, and examples are rare. However, when found, they are always of the extremely fine quality that one would expect.

ФАБЕРЖЕ

Plate 204

Left to right, top to bottom
Russian, art nouveau, star sapphire and diamond, carved moonstone, ruby and enamel, flower spray brooch. *£3,500 — £5,500*
Enamel, pearl and diamond, orchid pendant. c.1900
£3,000 — £5,000
Fine aquamarine and diamond, square cut-corner brooch, the aquamarine set in a diamond lattice-work mount, by Fabergé, c.1900.
No quote
Enamel, gold and diamond, rose bud brooch, hallmarked in Moscow.
£3,000 — £5,000
Cabochon sapphire, diamond and gold, circular open-work brooch, by Fabergé.
£1,500 — £2,000
Russian, apple green enamel and gold brooch, set with small diamonds.
£1,500 — £2,000
Cabochon sapphire, diamond, gold and enamel elongated diamond-shaped brooch, by Fabergé.
£2,000 — £3,000

(Wartski's and Private Collection)

261

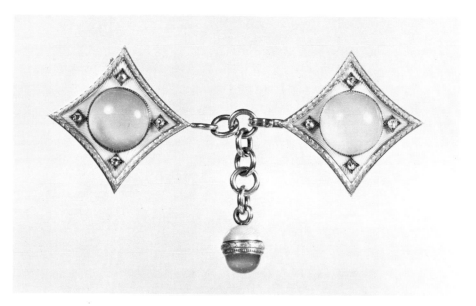

Plate 205

Early 20th century, gold and enamel fur clasp, set with agates and
diamonds, by Fabergé.
£6,000+
Fine Edwardian diamond, pearl and platinum choker, a fine example of
the trellis-work and milled setting typical of the early 1900s.
£10,000

(Private collection, The Purple Shop)

Plate 206

Art nouveau, 18ct. gold, opal and freshwater pearl
necklace, by Liberty & Co., c.1900.
£2,200 — £2,700

Plate 207

Left to right, top to bottom
Blue and green enamel, mother-of-pearl and silver wing brooch
£220 — £330
Amazonite, blue and green enamel and freshwater pearl pendant, set in silver and 18ct. gold.
£220 — £275
Amethyst and green enamel wing pendant in silver-gilt.
£225 — £280
Opal, blue and greenish enamel and crystal, open-wing brooch.
£550 — £650
Blue enamel brooch, designed as wings and a staff, set with a pearl and a crystal, the staff intertwined with a pale green and a blue enamel snake.
£250 — £300

All by Child & Child, c.1900.

(Courtesy of Antiquarius, The Purple Shop and Bellamy)

(Courtesy of Antiquarius, Bellamy and The Purple Shop)

Plate 208

Sapphire, pearl and enamel pendant in 9ct. gold, c.1900.
£250 — £300
Plique-à-jour enamel, mother-of-pearl and silver brooch, c.1910.
£250 — £300
Plique-à-jour enamel and pearl lotus flower pendant in silver-gilt. Egyptian influence,
c.1925.
£200 — £300
Gold, ruby and rose diamond brooch, French c.1900.
£400 — £500
Art nouveau metal pendant, a female profile, French c.1905.
£150 — £200
Plique-à-jour enamel and silver 'Egyptian' brooch, set with a cabochon garnet, c.1925.
£150 — £200
Freshwater pearl 'bunch of grapes' pendant with silvery-green enamel leaves, set in 14ct.
gold, French, c.1900.
£250 — £350

Plate 209

A fine art nouveau tropical butterfly brooch, in gold and diamonds with delicately coloured *plique-à-jour* enamels varying from carmine pink, to bronze, green and violet, giving an effect of iridescence, c.1905.

£20,000 — £30,000

A fine art nouveau dragonfly brooch in *plique-à-jour* enamels, set with a ruby, diamonds and emeralds, by Lalique.

£30,000 — £50,000

Plate 210

French, enamelled, peacock feather buckle, the centre set with green and blue 'peacock eye' paste, signed PF, dagger between, c.1900.
£300 — £500
French, coloured enamel, butterfly buckle in gilt metal, signed PF, dagger between, c.1900.
£300 — £500

Plate 211

Left to right, top to bottom

Blue and green enamel pendant, set in silver. c.1900.

£150 — £200

Blue enamel floral pendant, set in silver, c.1905.

£100 — £130

Oval silver pendant, set with mother-of-pearl, surrounded by blue and green enamel, with a pendant heart, c.1900 by S. & Co.

£175 — £220

Enamel mermaid pendant, set in silver.

£150 — £200

Opal and silver brooch.

£300 — £400

Silver bat brooch, set with a wood opal body and opal head.

£250 — £300

Blue and green enamelled necklace in silver, set with mother-of-pearl, c.1900 by Liberty & Co.

£340 — £390

Amethyst and purple enamel necklace in silver, c.1905 by Liberty & Co.

£575 — £675

(Private Collection, The Purple Shop)

Plate 212

Left to right, top to bottom
Art nouveau, *pâte de verre*,
pendants.
Insect pendant in shades of
yellow, green and brown.
£250 — £350
Dragonfly pendant in greens,
blues and browns.
£350 — £450
Insect pendant, browns, yellows
and oranges, signed A.V.N.
£350 — £450
Cicada pendant, purples,
browns, blues and black.
£450 — £550
Bat pendant, iridescent blues
and purples, on a silver chain.
£350 — £450
Scarab pendant, coloured with
iridescent blues and purples,
with a 9ct. gold setting.
£250 — £300

(Private Collection, The Purple Shop)

270

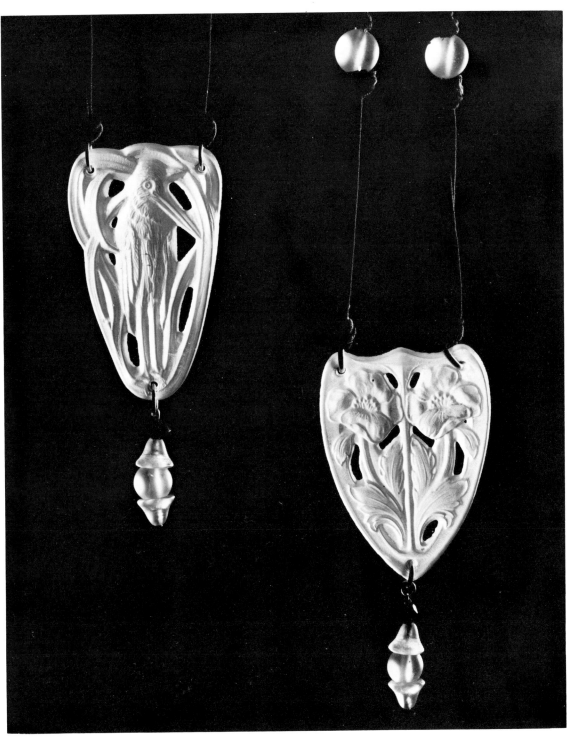

(*Antiquarius, Bellamy*)

Plate 213

Two pendants of frosted glass, one of a pelican, one of anemones, both French c.1920,
slightly larger than actual size.
£250 — £350

Plate 214

An opal, enamel and silver brooch by Liberty & Co.
£600 — £800
Silver and enamel pendant and necklace by Ramsden & Carr, c.1905.
£1,400 — £1,700
18ct. gold necklace, set with turquoises and freshwater pearls, by Liberty & Co.
£2,750 — £3,250
Enamel pendant with mother-of-pearl on silver chain, by Otto Prutscher.
£500 — £650
Scrolled 18ct. gold pendant set with mother-of-pearl and fire opals, by Edward Colonna.
£900 — £1,300
Plique-à-jour enamel pendant cum powder compact, set with long freshwater pearls between
the radiating enamelled sections.
£700 — £875

(Private collection, The Purple Shop)

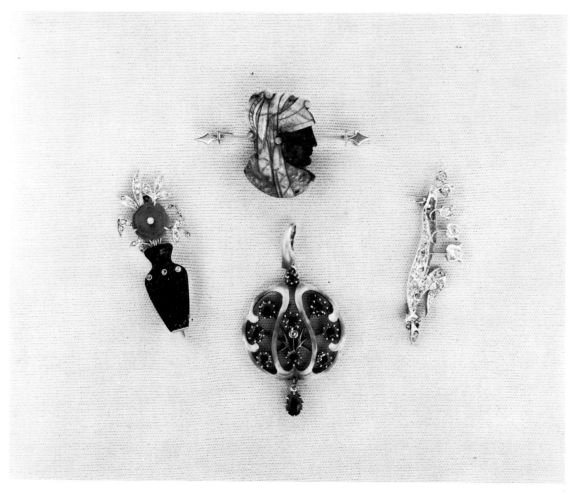

Plate 215

Top to bottom, left to right
Opal cameo mounted as a brooch on a gold pin, by Newman of Melbourne, c.1900. A good example
of carving, the head-dress of black opal carved from the matrix which forms the face.
£700 — £900
Art deco, lapis lazuli, vase brooch containing a cornelian flower with diamond set leaves. c.1930.
£950 — £1,300
Edwardian, diamond, lily-of-the-valley spray brooch, set in silver and gold.
£500 — £600
Art nouveau pendant of scrolled enamel set with Montana sapphires, c.1905. The delicate, almost
iridescent enamel sets off the metallic colour of the sapphires well.
£1,100 — £1,400

Plate 216

Left to right, top to bottom
Circular silver compact, designed to be worn as a pendant.
£140 — £160
Art nouveau pendant, the ivory face surrounded by a silver-gilt frame set with turquoises, garnets, emeralds and corals, on a silver-gilt chain with orange and green *plique-à-jour* enamel sections.
£650 — £850
Silver pocket-watch, signed 'Huguenin'.
£800 — £1,000
'Egyptian' head made of ivorine, set in gilt metal with red and white enamelled scarabs and lotus flowers.
£200 — £300
French silver and silver-gilt buckle set with opals, rubies, diamonds and sapphires.
£750 — £950

(The Purple Shop Private Collection)

Plate 217

Left to right, top to bottom
Green enamel flower brooch set with two cabochon amethysts in silver-gilt, c.1900.
£350 — £475
Plique-à-jour enamel vine leaf with seed pearl bunch of grapes suspending a green enamelled watch.
£850 — £950
Green enamel and mother-of-pearl pendant.
£350 — £500
Enamel brooch, set with cabochon garnets in silver-gilt
£350 — £500
Green enamel, lozenge-shaped brooch set with mother-of-pearl and marcasites.
£275 — £375
Green and yellow enamel pendant, set with an opal, marcasites, and pendent freshwater pearls.
£500 — £650
Enamel slide on a silver chain.
£200 — £250
Green and yellow enamel pendant set with marcasites, a paste and a freshwater pearl in silver-gilt.
£500 — £700
Blue enamel, wing-shaped pendant, set with mother-of-pearl in silver-gilt on a chain with baroque pearls inset.
£500 — £700
Enamel and *plique-à-jour* enamelled butterfly set with a cabochon garnet in silver-gilt.
£550 — £650
Enamel eel brooch in silver with chrysoprase eyes.
£550 — £650
Enamel dragonfly brooch, set in silver-gilt.
£500 — £600
Pink and blue enamel pendant, set with blue pastes and seed pearls in silver.
£550 — £650　　　*(Private collection, The Purple Shop)*

Plate 218

French art nouveau, horn birds and insects
Dragonfly brooch.
£75 — £110
Dragonfly brooch.
£75 — £110
Dragonfly pendant, by Bonté.
£250 — £400
Reverse of above, showing signature.
Moth brooch.
£100 — £150
Flying duck.
£75 — £125

(The Purple Shop Private Collection)

Plate 219

Left to right, top to bottom
Onyx, mother-of-pearl and silver ring, in a foliate setting.
£250 — £300
Sapphire and 18ct. gold ring, by Henry Wilson.
£750 — £1,000
Opal and silver ring, by Henry Wilson.
£550 — £750
Pearl and silver floral ring, by de Monville.
£350 — £450
Turquoise and silver, rectanguler shaped ring.
£160 — £220

Plate 220

A group of art nouveau and 20th century enamelled animals, in silver or metal, using a variety of techniques and materials, including turquoises (with *plique-à-jour* enamel — butterfly brooch inside necklace), real butterfly wings, enamels and glass.
Enamelled brooches *£40 — £120*
Necklace *£80 — £150*
Plique-à-jour butterfly *£250 — £400*

(Courtesy of Antiquarius, Tony & Sara, The Purple Shop, Bellamy, Chimera and Thesaurus)

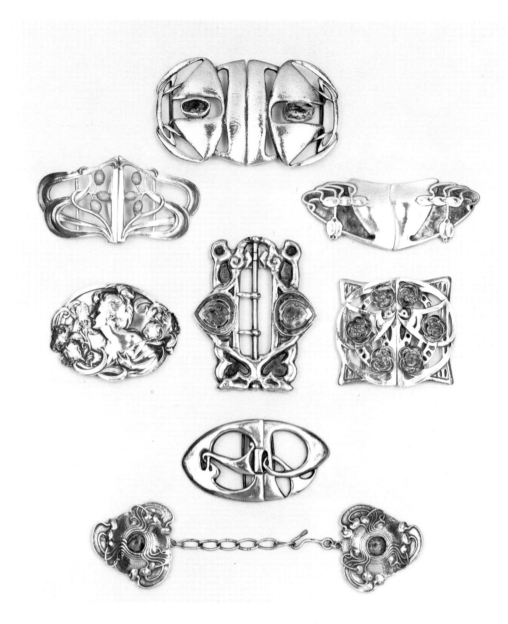

(Private collection, The Purple Shop)

Plate 221

Left to right, top to bottom
Varying in price from £250 — £600 each
Turquoise matrix and hammered silver buckle, marked Cymric.
Opal and open-work silver buckle, by Liberty & Co.
Silver and enamel buckle, by Liberty & Co.
Silver buckle with female bust, French, factory-made.
Silver buckle with green, red and blue enamel, by Liberty & Co.
Open-work silver buckle with green, brown and blue enamel, by Liberty & Co.
Silver buckle formed of the letters 'ER' for Edward VII, unmarked, but probably made to commemorate his coronation in 1901.
Silver cloak fastener set with turquoise matrix, c.1905, marked Cymric.

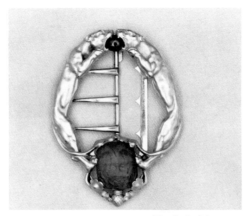

(Sotheby's)

(The Purple Shop Private Collection)

(The Purple Shop Private Collection)

Plate 222

Top to bottom
Art nouveau gold buckle in the form of two lionesses fighting over a
cornelian heart, the base formed of a moulded, olive green, glass lion's
mask, by Boucheron. Exhibited at their exhibition in Paris in 1900.
£5,000+
Agate and silver buckle of floral design, by Vever of Paris.
£1,200 — £1,700
Silver buckle in three sections, set with mother-of-pearl, made in London
in 1902 by William Mutton & Sons.
£750 — £850

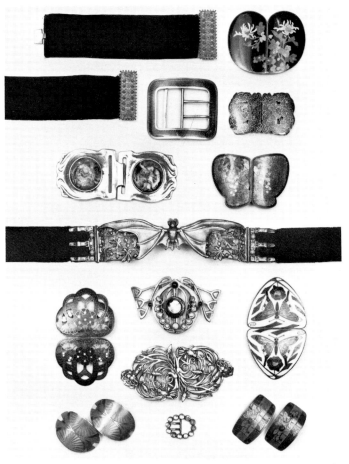

(Courtesy of Antiquarius, Bellamy, The Purple Shop, John Taylor Tony & Sara and Thesaurus)

Plate 223

Left to right, top to bottom
A pair of Georgian, metal-gilt, bracelet clasps, on black velvet, c.1830.
£70 — £100
19th century, Chinese enamel buckle, set in metal and silver.
£80 — £130
Enamelled metal buckle.
£50 — £90

Enamelled metal buckle of floral design.
£70 — £100
Art nouveau, silver and enamelled buckle, the centre enamelled with the figures of Echo and Narcissus.
£280 — £400
Late 19th century, enamel and metal buckle, silver-backed.
£75 — £100
Art nouveau metal 'bat' buckle set with a turquoise-coloured paste.
£140 — £180
Enamel and metal buckle of open-work design.
£80 — £120
Art nouveau metal buckle, set with pastes.
£70 — £120
Enamel and silver buckle, butterfly design.
£150 — £200
Art nouveau, silver buckle, with carnation design.
£150 — £200
A pair of art deco silver and enamel shoe buckles.
£50 — £90
Moonstone and silver buckle.
£90 — £120
A pair of art deco metal and enamel shoe buckles.
£70 — £110

(Christie's)

Plate 224

A rare pair of Georgian diamond pear-shaped pavé set buckles, c.1800.
£5,000 — £6,000

(N. Bloom and Christie's)

Plate 225

Edwardian, diamond, open-work pendant in the form of a bow with pendent quatrefoil and drops, set with mixed brilliant and rose-cut diamonds in platinum.

£3,500 — £4,000

Diamond and cabochon ruby, trellis-work necklace, set in platinum. If broken up, this could be made into an attractive brooch and earrings, four ruby and diamond cluster rings and a range of hundreds of small extra diamonds.

£40,000 — £60,000

(Courtesy of Antiquarius, Thesaurus, The Purple Shop, Tony & Sara and Private Collection)

Plate 226

Early 20th century, peridot, diamond and pearl pendant in 15ct. gold. *£275 — £375*
Edwardian, peridot, pink tourmaline and aquamarine open-work pendant in 9ct. gold.
£200 — £250
Gold spider's web pendant, with a turquoise and pearl set spider. *£200 — £250*
Amethyst and pearl, open-work pendant in 9ct. gold. *£200 — £300*
Circular, 9ct. gold pendant set with a peridot and pearls suspended from a peridot collet.
£180 — £250
Opal, ruby and pearl, clover leaf pendant set in 18ct. gold gold. *£250 — £300*
Opal and ruby set, spider and fly pendant in 9ct. gold. *£200 — £300*
Montana sapphire, open-work pendant set with rose diamonds in gold. *£700 — £900*
Opal, ruby and diamond set, clover leaf pendant in yellow gold. *£250 — £350*
Circular, diamond and open-work pendant in 18ct. gold. *£175 — £275*
9ct. gold, scrolled pendant set with a centre amethyst. *£200 — £275*
Sapphire and pearl, open-work pendant in 18ct. gold with a sapphire drop. *£275 — £350*
Garnet and pearl set, circular floral pendant in 9ct. gold. *£200 — £270*
Aquamarine and pearl pendant in 9ct. gold. *£200 — £300*
(Allow £45 — £85 for chains)

(*Cameo Corner*)

Plate 227

Left to right, top to bottom
Carved moonstone pendant with drop, set in a frame of diamonds and pearls in platinum, c.1910.
£3,500 — £4,000
Floral drop pendant, set with diamonds, *calibré* cut rubies and a pearl in platinum, c.1905.
£3,000 — £4,000
Black pearl and diamond, drop pendant with a diamond ribbon top. (The pendant chain is showing behind the pearl.)
£2,000 — £2,500
Aquamarine and diamond cluster ring.
£1,200 — £1,700
Edwardian 'Suffragette' ring of pink topaz surrounded by green garnets and diamonds, c.1913 (pink, green and white were the Suffragette colours).
£2,500 — £3,000
A pair of aquamarine and diamond drop earrings, c.1910.
£2,500 — £3,000
Decorated, ribbon bow brooch set with brilliant and rose-cut diamonds in platinum, c.1910.
£3,000 — £5,000
Late 19th century, aquamarine and diamond brooch of open-work design, by R.S. & E.
£1,400 — £1,800
Late Victorian, flexible diamond bracelet of ribbon design, set with brilliants and rose diamonds in silver and gold, c.1890.
£6,000

(Sotheby's and Christie's)

Plate 228

Edwardian, diamond, lace ribbon bow brooch, bordered with small *calibré* emeralds, set in platinum,
c.1905. The setting is of good quality and the mount is curved, giving the brooch shape.
£15,000 — £20,000

Edwardian, diamond, bandeau head ornament formed of open-work floral oval panels linked with
fine sections of trellis work, c.1905.
£18,000 — £25,000

Plate 229

Edwardian, pearl and diamond, ribbon bow brooch, the long ribbon
pendants are convertible into earrings, and the milled setting is
typical of the Edwardian period, c.1910.
£12,000 — £20,000

(Antiquarius, Bellamy)

Plate 230

An Edwardian, cut steel, metal and leather belt, showing the clasp and the back section of
cut steel.
£100 — £200

Plate 231

Diamond, fringe necklace set
with baguette and brilliant-cut
diamonds.
£20,000 — £30,000
Diamond brooch, designed as
a buckle and scarf, set with
pavé set brilliants and a fringe
of baguettes.
£12,000 — £15,000

(Christie's)

Plate 232

Art deco diamond and emerald bead necklace, also forming two bracelets.
£70,000 — £100,000

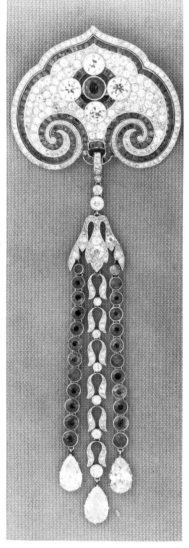

Plate 233

Left to right

Art deco, sapphire and diamond, drop brooch/pendant, set with two *briolette* cut sapphire drops, c.1925.

£150,000 — £200,000

Art deco, sapphire and diamond brooch/pendant of good quality, in the Indian style, c.1920.

£35,000 — £50,000

Green garnet and diamond, floral spray brooch. Green (demantoid) garnets of this size are unusual.

£20,000 — £25,000

Plate 234

Art deco suite of brooch, pendant and earrings in onyx, diamonds and platinum,
by Cartier.
£35,000 — £45,000

Plate 235

Art deco, aquamarine and diamond necklace
of formal scroll design, mounted in platinum.
£12,000 — £15,000

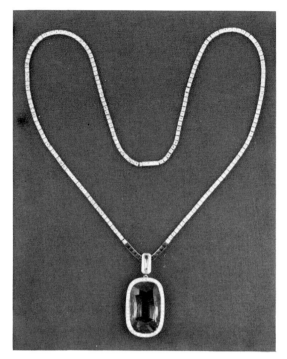

Plate 236

A fine 20th century, sapphire and diamond
pendant with line necklace, by Cartier.
£150,000 — £250,000

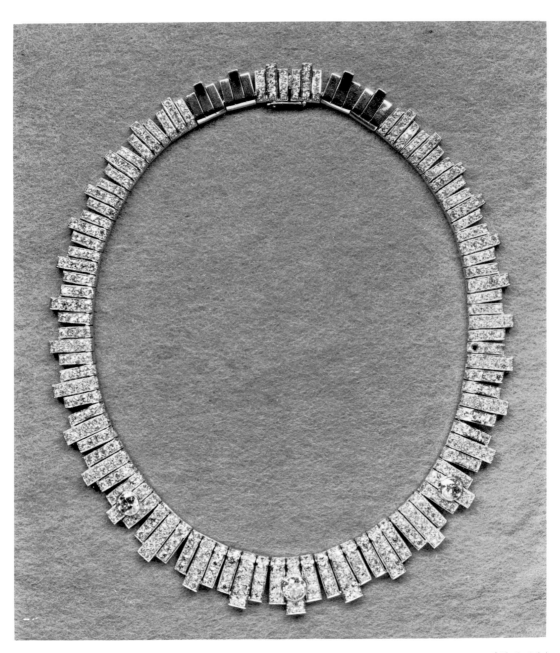

Plate 237

Art deco, diamond flange necklace, set with brilliant-cut diamonds in gold, by Boucheron.
£25,000 — £45,000

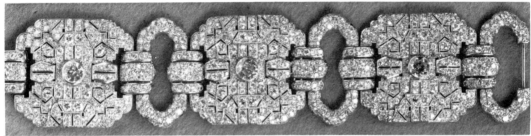

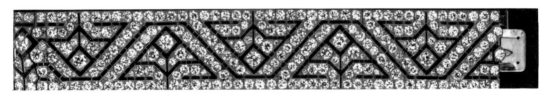

(Christie's)

Plate 238

Top to bottom
Diamond tiara, formed of twisted scrolls, c.1935.
£12,000 — £15,000
Art deco diamond bracelet, formed of six linked sections, set in platinum, c.1920.
£12,000 — £18,000
Diamond bracelet of open triangular design, set in platinum, by Van Cleef & Arpels.
£7,000 — £12,000
Art deco, diamond, link bracelet.
£9,000 — £14,000
An important emerald and brilliant-cut diamond bracelet of twelve emeralds and ten
diamonds. A typical piece of jewellery which might be bought at auction 'for break'.
£30,000 — £50,000

Plate 239

Left to right, top to bottom
Peridot and diamond brooch with peridot drops, set in silver and gold.
£2,000 — £3,000
Art deco, sapphire and diamond drop earrings, c.1930.
£5,000+
Diamond and emerald, lily spray brooch, set in platinum, c.1920.
£1,200 — £1,600
Art deco, jade and diamond brooch, set in platinum.
£700 — £850
Early 20th century brooch and earrings of frosted crystal, amethysts and diamonds.
£1,600 — £2,200
Art deco, jardinière brooch, set in platinum with diamonds and a variety of coloured stones.
£1,900 — £2,400
Art deco, pavé set diamond, hexagonal pendant with centre bar, in platinum.
£5,000+
Diamond, sapphire and ruby Union Jack, c.1920.
£1,700 — £2,000
Art deco, sapphire and diamond, rayed, oblong plaque brooch.
£6,000+
Art deco, aquamarine, emerald and diamond buckle brooch.
£7,200 — £8,000
Edwardian, diamond and demantoid garnet open-work bar brooch, set in platinum, c.1905.
£3,000 — £4,000

(N. Bloom)

(N. Bloom)

(Michael Poynder)

(N. Bloom)

(Michael Poynder)

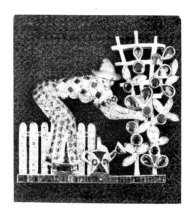

(N. Bloom)

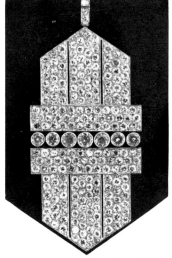

(Christie's)

(Michael Poynder)

(Christie's)

(Christie's)

(N. Bloom)

Plate 240

Left to right, top to bottom
Brown and yellow enamelled belt buckle, set in silver
£100 — £140
Red and black enamelled buckle in chrome
£35 — £60
Elongated octagonal buckle, enamelled in yellow, brown, blue, green and black, set in brass
£50 — £70
Blue and red enamelled buckle in chrome
£40 — £60
Black onyx, open circle brooch, set with a bar of rose diamonds in platinum, c.1920. by Cartier.
£1,500 — £1,750
Multi-coloured paste necklace of floral design, set in silver, c.1925.
£200 — £250
Necklace of geometric design, set with cornelians and onyx in silver.
£250 — £350
Multi-coloured enamel necklace, set in gilt metal.
£150 — £200
Yellow, black and blue enamelled figure, set in silver.
£150 — £200
Blue enamel yacht brooch in chrome, c.1930.
£75 — £100
(Courtesy of Antiquarius, Bellamy, The Purple Shop and E. Ashley Cooper)

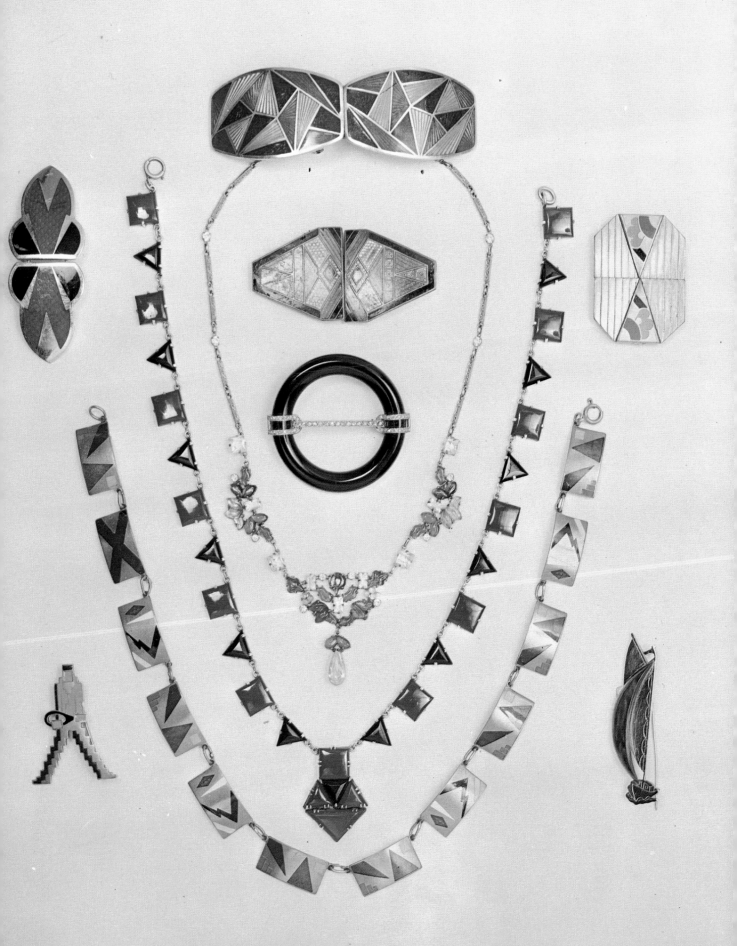

Plate 241

An art deco white paste, black and yellow, plastic necklace backed with silver-plated metal, the sections strung on a silver chain. Well-made art deco costume jewellery is currently very fashionable.
£300 — £400

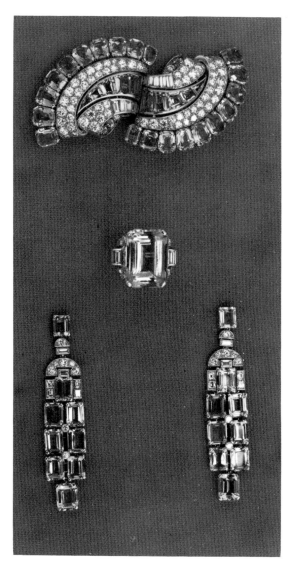

Plate 242

Left to right, top to bottom
Art deco, suite of aquamarine and diamond, double clip brooch, ring and earrings, mounted
in platinum, c.1925.
£8,500 — £12,000
Art deco, ruby and diamond necklace, set with *calibré* cut rubies and diamonds, on a white
gold chain, c.1940.
£15,000 — £25,000
Ruby and diamond ring, set with nine rubies and seven diamonds, in yellow gold, c.1940.
£2,300 — £3,000

Plate 243

This plate is representative of the craze for Egyptian style jewellery which swept Europe after the discovery of the Tut-ankh-amun tomb in 1925.

Plique-à-jour enamel, paste and silver-gilt, Ba-bird brooch.
£375 — £625

Carved amethyst scarab, ruby and rose diamond, drop pendant in gold.
£600 — £750

Enamel and silver-plated circular buckle.
£55 — £95

Carved cornelian, scarab ring with 22ct. gold mount.
£325 — £375

Carved green turquoise, scarab ring in 14ct. gold.
£325 — £375

Faïence scarab ring in 9ct. gold.
£100 — £150

Cornelian, chrysoprase and enamel, link bracelet in silver plate, the cornelian and chrysoprases carved as scarabs.
£150 — £250

Enamel and silver-gilt, oval plaque bracelet.
£120 — £180

Enamel and silver-gilt bracelet with Egyptian landscapes.
£120 — £180

Bloodstone scarab pendant in gold.
£200 — £275

Bracelet set with lapis lazuli in silver-gilt, and enamelled, copied from bracelets worn by the High Priest Pi-nudjem II from Thebes.
£600 — £850

Egyptian silver 'head' brooch.
£60 — £80

Oval, open-work, gilt metal pendant of an Egyptian figure.
£50 — £70

Scarab brooch with *plique-à-jour* enamel wings and enamelled body.
£180 — £240

Silver and enamel brooch with a pyramid in the centre.
£55 — £85

Enamel and silver-gilt, 'Egyptian' mummy-case empty.
£40 — £60

Enamel and silver-gilt, 'Egyptian' Moses in a Basket.
£40 — £60

Enamel and silver-gilt mummy in a case.
£50 — £90

Silver-gilt Moses in a Basket, open.
£40 — £75

Silver-gilt mummy and case.
£50 — £70

Blue enamel and metal plaque bracelet in the Egyptian style.
£50 — £70

(Courtesy of Antiquarius, The Purple Shop, Bellamy, Thesaurus, and Chimera)

Plate 244

Bangle of green Bakelite and lacquered brass, the centre opening as a compact, c.1930.
£160 — £200
Bakelite dress clip, carved with initial 'J'.
£20 — £40
Wood and chrome dress clip.
£10 — £20
Silvered glass dress clip.
£20 — £40
Mirror-backed glass and silver pendant on a chain.
£70 — £100
Chrome and Bakelite, stylised cherry pendant on chain.
£100 — £140

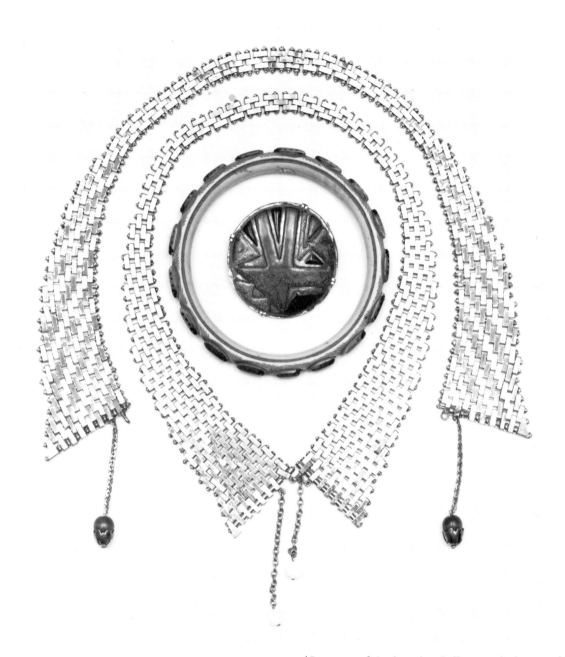

Plate 245

Outside to inside
Art deco, flexible, chrome collar, stove enamelled.
£110 — £150
Art deco, flexible, chrome collar, stove enamelled.
£110 — £150
Plastic ladybird bangle.
£25 — £40
Art deco, Limoges enamel and silver brooch, by Fauré, c.1925.
£250 — £350

Plate 246

Chrome and plastic, banded, cigarette holder.
£20 — £50
Circular plastic, solid scent jar.
£20 — £50
Silver and amber cigarette holder with enamelled centre section.
£20 — £50
Long, green and red enamel, silver cigarette holder.
£20 — £50
Enamel, silver and plastic cigarette holder.
£20 — £50
Chrome and plastic etui.
£20 — £50
Glass scent flask in plastic case, of Japanese influence.
£20 — £50
Circular plastic, solid scent jar.
£20 — £50
Long plastic, bamboo cigarette holder.
£20 — £50
Silver and green enamel lipstick case.
£20 — £50

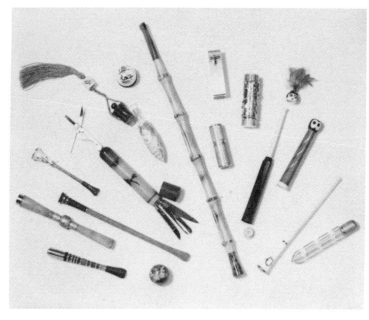

(Antiquarius, Bellamy and The Purple Shop)

Silver and gold rectangular lipstick case with *calibré* ruby catch.
£200 — £300
Silver, gold and cabochon sapphire lipstick case with floral motif, by Boucheron.
£375 — £475
Plastic cigarette holder, open for use.
£20 — £50
Plastic cigarette holder, closed.
£20 — £50
Gold, enamel and ivorine cigarette holder.
£20 — £50
Green and white enamelled glass scent flask, with enamelled silver top.
£20 — £50

Plate 247

(Courtesy of Antiquarius, Bellamy, The Purple Shop and Thesaurus)

Left to right, top to bottom
Green enamel, silver and gilt lacquer vanity mirror.
£30 — £40
Black enamel and silver Swiss watch.
£175 — £225
Duck-egg blue enamel and silver-gilt compact, French.
£80 — £100
Chrome and plastic watch on leather strap.
£60 — £80
Marcasite ring watch.
£75 — £100
Chrome and black leather clip watch.
£50 — £65
Turquoise enamel and silver compact, English.
£70 — £85
Bakelite vanity mirror.
£30 — £45
Purple enamel and silver-gilt powder puff.
£50 — £90
Yellow enamel and silver powder puff, with a lipstick case concealed in a yellow tassel.
£90 — £120
Diamond and white gold lapel watch.
£900 — £1,300
9ct. gold watch, engraved on the reverse '1947', English.
£250 — £310
Silver-gilt and enamel 'Egyptian' compact, c.1925.
£90 — £120
Silver and enamel compact, with a bird and flowers, English.
£75 — £95

20th Century Paste Jewellery

(Courtesy of Antiquarius, Bellamy, John Taylor, The Purple Shop, Tony & Sara and Lynda Perkin Antiques)

Plate 248

Left to right, top to bottom
Art deco, black plastic and paste
buckle.
£40 — £60
Art deco, paste, chrysoprase
and marcasite brooch in silver.
£120 — £140
Red and white paste, stylised
bow brooch, c.1940.
£90 — £120
Green, red and white paste,
butterfly brooch in silver-gilt.
£90 — £120
Green, red and white paste
lizard in silver.
£75 — £100
Painted metal peacock set with
pastes.
£30 — £50
Silver-plated buckle, set with a
cornelian and pastes, signed
'T.B.'
£100 — £120
Silver and gilt metal dress clip,
set with pastes, c.1940.
£30 — £45
Art deco, paste and metal, chain
link necklet.
£50 — £70
Paste drop earrings, set in
metal, c.1940.
£30 — £60
Blue and white paste brooch, set
in silver, c.1930.
£120 — £175
Green and white paste bracelet
and clasp, c.1930.
£80 — £100
Art deco, black glass, paste and
metal stylised flower brooch.
£50 — £60
Blue and white paste on metal
flexible bracelet, c.1940.
£75 — £95

(Antiquarius, The Purple Shop and Marie Mills Private Coll.)

Plate 249

Silver cloak fastener/brooch, set with moonstones and labradorite. Could be worn as a brooch
or cloak-clasp since the fastenings are on each top section.
£750 — £1,000

Silver and moonstone necklace, with a British Import Mark for 1961. (Most jewellery imported
into England which is less than one hundred years old normally has to be sent to the Assay Office
who will then stamp the appropriate control marks. Therefore, an Import Mark for 1961 only
means that the piece entered England at that date and it could have been made some years before.)
£750 — £1,000

Moonstone

Moonstones are a translucent bluish-white colour and belong to the feldspar family, which also includes labradorite and amazonite. Of these three best known feldspars, moonstone is the most used in jewellery. Better quality moonstones are a bluish colour, with a fine silvery sheen called adularescence, while poor quality stones are a dull, dirty grey with yellowish tinges and are almost transparent. Moonstones were popular at the end of the last century and were used in art nouveau jewellery in conjunction with garnets, turquoises, fire opals and enamels, etc.

The major source, as for so many gemstones, is Sri Lanka, although moonstones also come from Madagascar, Burma, India and Tanzania. The Madagascan moonstones have a tendency to be golden yellow, as have the Burmese stones which also show a cat's eye effect, but not as strongly as the chrysoberyl cat's eye. They are always cut "en cabochon" to show their adularescence.

Technicalities: Chemical composition: potash feldspar (orthoclase), $(KAlSi_3O_8)$. Crystal structure: monoclinic. Hardness: 6. S.G.: 2.56-2.59. R.I.: 1.52-1.525.

Labradorite is a greyish feldspar with iridescent flashes of greens and blues reflected from within the stone. It has the effect of butterflies' wings. It was used in art nouveau and art deco period jewellery and first came from the coast of Labrador, hence its name.

Amazonite is little used in jewellery.

Sybil Dunlop

Plate 250

Examples of well-designed and well made jewellery, showing the sensitive use of stones with silver and gold for which Sybil Dunlop's work is noted. Only a few of her earlier pieces were signed and their style is not so formed as her later unsigned pieces. Mark S.D.

Silver pendant, set with two hexagonal-cut amethysts, opals, garnets, chalcedony and tourmalines, c.1935.
£800 — £1,100

Moonstone, mother-of-pearl, crystal and silver cross.
£550 — £650

Amethyst and silver, open circle, ivy leaf brooch.
£250 — £400

Open circle, floral brooch in silver and 15ct. gold set with crystals, aquamarines, tourmalines, emeralds and chalcedony.
£575 — £700

15ct. gold, floral pendant and chain, set with moonstones, emeralds and an amethyst.
£2,200 — £2,700

15ct. gold and silver, open circle brooch, set with tourmalines, chrysoprases and moonstones, by Henry Wilson.
£600 — £725

(Private Collection, The Purple Shop)

Plate 251

Left to right, top to bottom
Rose quartz, chalcedony, chrysoprase, freshwater pearl and green enamel brooch, unsigned, c.1940.
£200 — £240
Blue, green and orange enamel, pansy brooch, set with two freshwater pearls in silver, 1937.
£200 — £240
Pink and blue enamel, 'Cherub' pendant in moonstone, rose quartz, amethyst and silver frame, on a chain.
£300 — £375
Green and pink enamel flower, set as a brooch in a silver and pearl frame, 1922.
£225 — £325
Green and orange enamel, 'Poppies' pendant, set with chalcedony and imitation pearls in silver as a necklace, 1935.
£300 — £400

(The Purple Shop Private Collection)

Opals

Opals occur in four main colours: white, black and green, which throw out vivid colour flashes, and the translucent red variety known as fire opal. Opal was held in esteem as a gemstone until the 19th century when the influence of Sir Walter Scott's novel *Anne of Geierstein* made people think of it as unlucky and malignant.

Opal contains a varying amount of water, and extreme changes of temperature will cause it to crack. As it is not particularly hard, it will not only crack and sometimes break, but will also scratch easily if it is roughly treated. This may well have added to the superstition that opal is unlucky, as from early times it has always been considered that to break anything precious will bring bad luck. Emeralds and mirrors are obvious examples of this, as both also have a high fracture property.

The "play of colour" of opal produces beautiful effects of iridescence and the term "opalescence" has come into our language because of it. Opal also occurs in fossilised wood, sometimes used in jewellery. This can be very attractive, as the seams of brightly coloured opal, veined through the dark wood, have the appearance of abstract painting. Water opals are very pale, almost clear, and have a poor play of colour.

Opals, which have been mined in Hungary and Czechoslovakia since Roman times, are characteristically a creamy colour, with small points of red, blue and green; these are referred to as "harlequin opals". Those mined in Mexico range in colour from yellow to deep red, and are known as fire opals. They are not used in jewellery a great deal as the colour is difficult to wear, but they can look magnificent on dark-haired and dark-skinned women. Australia is a major source of fine opals and they have been mined there since the 1870s. The most famous location is Lightning Ridge in New South Wales, and black opals of top gem quality come from there. Two other famous mines, better known for white opals, are Coober Pedy and Andamooka. Opals occur at comparatively shallow levels, and there are no great mining problems except for the extreme temperatures encountered, often as high as 130°F. This in itself can cause an opal to crack when it is brought to the surface.

Only fire opals are faceted, either brilliant or step-cut. All other opals are cut "en cabochon" or as beads, although where they occur in strong bands of colour, they are sometimes cameo cut, or carved to form figures or animals. Wood opals may be cut "en cabochon" or flat cut as pendants mounted in gold or silver and they were very popular in art nouveau jewellery.

Technicalities: Chemical composition: a hydrated silica (SiO_2nH_2O). Crystal structure: amorphous considered to be a solidified jelly. Hardness: 5½-6½. S.G.: 1.98-2.20. R.I.: 1.44-1.46. Doublets and triplets are common. They are composed of a thin slice of opal backed with opal matrix or wood opal, and black plastic or black mother-of-pearl. When buying what purports to be a black opal, it is best to see the stone unmounted. Synthetic opals are now being produced in the laboratory and marketed as Gilson opals; they are indistinguishable from natural opal except by laboratory-testing.

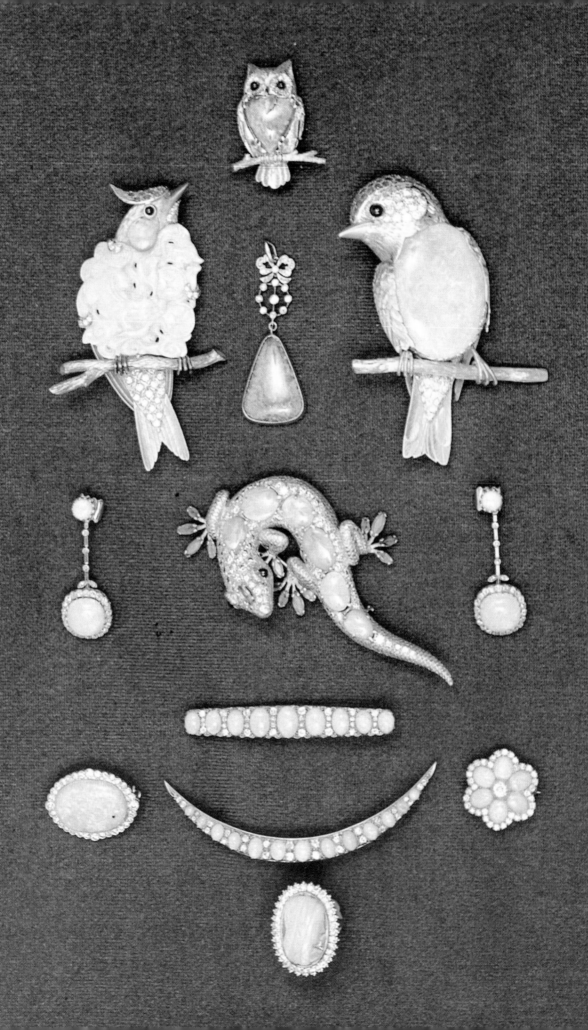

Plate 252

Left to right, top to bottom
'Peacock' opal diamond and gold owl brooch.
£1,500 — £2,000
Carved opal set in a brooch designed as a crested bird, with diamonds and rubies in gold.
£3,500 — £4,500
Edwardian diamond and black opal triplet pendant.
£475 — £575
Opal, ruby, diamond and gold bird brooch.
£5,000+
A pair of opal and diamond drop earrings.
£1,600 — £1,800
Opal, emerald, diamond and gold lizard brooch
£4,500 — £6,000
Edwardian, opal and diamond, bar brooch, c.1900.
£1,500 — £2,000
Oval opal and diamond cluster brooch, set in platinum.
£2,000 — £2,500
Late Victorian, opal and diamond, large shallow crescent brooch, c.1895.
£1,000 — £1,500
Opal and diamond, traditional flower cluster brooch.
£1,000 — £1,500
Art nouveau, opal cameo ring in traditional diamond cluster mount. (Stolen from Phillips, Son & Neale in February 1976.)
£900 — £1,400

(Courtesy of B. Barnett Ltd. and Michael Poynder)

(S.J. Phillips)

Plate 253

A pair of diamond earrings set with baguette and brilliant-cut diamonds in a geometric design.
£1,400 — £1,800

A large, sapphire and diamond, flower brooch, the flower composed of an exceptional range of pavé set, *calibré* cut sapphires with a brilliant-cut diamond cluster centre, the stem of baguette diamonds with two marquise diamonds designed as buds.
£30,000 — £50,000

An unusual pendant of pink tourmaline and jade pebbles, set with rose diamonds.
£2,500 — £3,000

Diamond bracelet, each linking section formed of brilliants and baguettes.
£6,500 — £8,500

Diamond and sapphire brooch, set with marquise, brilliant and baguette-cut diamonds, the sapphires *calibré* cut.
£6,000 — £7,000

Circular, carved emerald, set in a diamond rectangular brooch, the emerald forming the flowerhead surrounded by diamond leaves with two small sections of black enamel, in a milled setting.
£2,500 — £3,500

Emerald and diamond, graduated, open oval brooch.
£5,000 — £6,000

Diamond clip brooch incorporating diamonds of 'fancy' cuts such as trapeze and triangular, and also a half brilliant as well as the more conventional brilliants and baguettes, by Cartier.
£3,000 — £4,000

Plate 254

Top to bottom
Ruby and diamond, double clip brooch in white gold.
£20,000 — £30,000
Diamond, double clip brooch, set with brilliant and baguette-cut diamonds.
£6,000+
Diamond and sapphire brooch, designed as two lilies, pavé set with brilliants and baguette-cut diamonds, c.1935.
£12,000
Sapphire and diamond, double clip brooch, set with marquise, brilliant and baguette-cut diamonds.
£15,000 — £25,000
The quality of stones in clip brooches of this type is frequently mixed, and they are often broken up today and the stones reset into more fashionable pieces of jewellery.

Plate 255

Jardinière brooch, set with white and coloured diamonds, rubies, emeralds and sapphires in a baguette-cut diamond vase.

£8,000

Stomacher brooch/pendant, set with cabochon-cut emeralds, rubies, sapphires and brilliant-cut diamonds, by Van Cleef & Arpels.

£12,000 — £20,000

A pair of diamond, ruby, emerald and sapphire parakeets as a brooch, separating into two clips.

£9,000

Diamond, sapphire, carved emerald and ruby jardinière brooch, the vase formed by a large single diamond.

£12,000+

Art deco, stylised jardinière brooch, set with baguette and brilliant-cut diamonds, ruby and sapphire flowers with carved emerald leaves.

£4,000 — £5,000

A smart, diamond buckle brooch with carved emeralds, sapphires and rubies.

£4,000 — £5,000

Sapphire, emerald and diamond earrings in gold.

£3,000

This plate shows 20th century diamond and coloured stone jewellery at its best. Each piece is imaginative, and the work of a craftsman.

(S.J. Phillips)

Plate 256

Left to right, top to bottom
Stylised, tied knot brooch, set with diamonds.
Traditional, diamond, floral cluster brooch.
Stylised, diamond, tied ribbon brooch, pavé set.
Diamond, knotted 'waterfall' brooch.
Diamond flower brooch.
Diamond circular 'cascade' brooch.
Diamond, tied ribbon brooch, c.1930.
Diamond, S-shaped, double clip brooch. This brooch will separate to form two individual
clips of identical design.
One half of a diamond double clip brooch. It may equally well be worn on its own.
Diamond scrolled double clip brooch.
£2,000 — £4,000
These brooches of the 1930s, '40s and '50s are set in white gold or platinum.

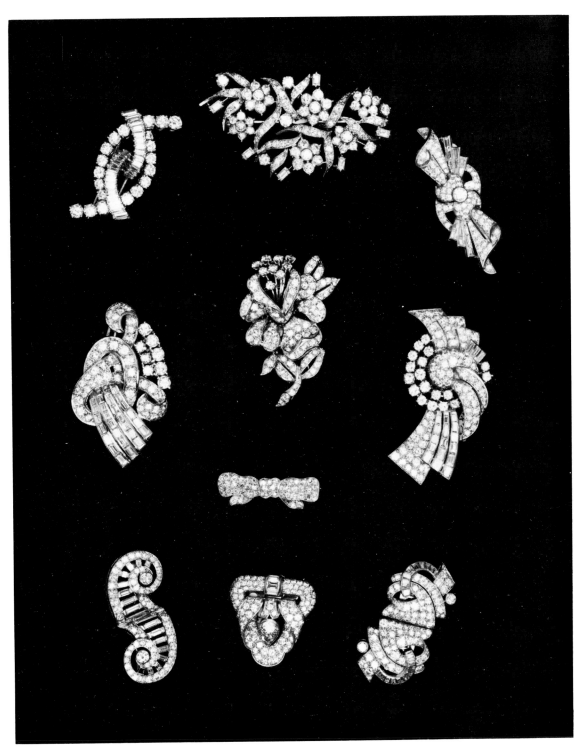

South-West American Indian Jewellery

In the middle of the 19th century, Mexicans, and the Navajo Indians of New Mexico and Arizona, started trading silver trinkets for horses. By 1890, most Indian settlements (pueblos) were producing these trinkets in their own styles, made out of U.S. or Mexican dollars. They decorated necklaces, rings and buckles with roughly polished pieces of locally mined turquoise.

In 1890 the U.S. Government banned this defamation of the American currency, and by 1930, when the Mexicans followed suit, white traders had already started to increase considerably the import of silver to meet the demand for native jewellery. Little of the jewellery made at the end of the 19th century was produced commercially, but over the last seventy-five years other crafts, such as potting, carving and weaving, have given way to the more lucrative silver-work. Most jewellery craftsmen have normal jobs as well, using their skills as silversmiths and stone cutters to supplement their incomes, as they find a ready market for their output in North America, and, more recently, in Europe.

The Santo Domingans make many of the shell and turquoise bead necklaces and supply other tribes, as well as taking their wares to sell in other parts of America. The Navajo, Hopi and Zuni tribes produce the most distinctive silver-work. The Navajo has the largest population of a total of thirty-nine tribes. However, many people are beginning to leave the reserves and of the 80,000 who remain, only 2% work in silver. The design of their jewellery is simple and massive, although the early work was light and hammered out very thinly, due to the shortage of silver. The Navajo was the first tribe to use sand-casting, in 1895. The best known Navajo silver design is the squash blossom necklace (Plate 257), with a crescent-shaped Naja hanging from its centre.

The Hopi tribe is known for overlay designs. In 1938 the museum of Northern Arizona started to encourage this tribe to translate its pottery designs into jewellery using the overlay technique. A fretted piece of silver is sweated to a solid base plate. A pitted decoration is emphasised by blackening it with liver of sulphur, deepening the three-dimensional effect. Very little use is made of stones in this work.

The Zuni tribe relies mainly on the manufacture of jewellery for its income. About a fifth of the population of 5,000 work as stone-cutters and as silversmiths. By 1890 they had developed a distinctive style, making use of clusters and rows of small turquoises, delicately set in finely worked silver. In 1935 they started using channel setting. A piece was prepared rather as in *cloisonné* enamel, but instead of enamelling, the spaces between the silver walls were filled with cut pieces of jet, shell and turquoise and firmly glued, nowadays using modern adhesives. The whole surface was then polished and a very colourful mosaic effect achieved. Examples of this jewellery, recently made, are being sold extensively in Europe today but at inflated prices.

Plate 257

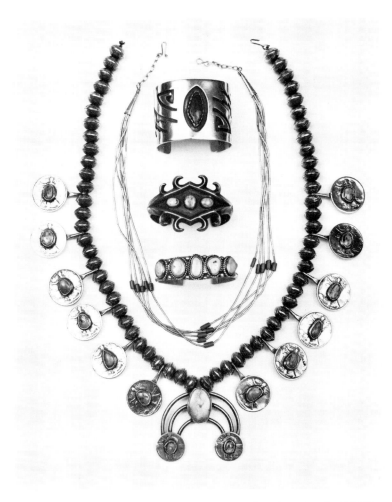

(Antiquarius, Stall M1)

Top to bottom

Hopi Indian silver bangle with turquoise matrix centre, made by Begay. (His family is well known for traditional craftsmanship.)

£500 — £600

Navajo Indian, dead pawn silver and turquoise sand-cast bangle, made in the 1940s.

£300 — £400

Navajo Indian, dead pawn bangle, five pieces of turquoise matrix set in silver.

£350 — £450

Santa Domingan silver 'Heishi' (water-cascade necklace), made from small silver cylindrical beads with larger coral ones in between. A traditional piece of contemporary manufacture.

£180 — £220

Navajo Indian squash necklace, the beads and discs are made from American silver dimes, quarters, half dollar and dollar pieces, inlaid with turquoise matrix. The latest date on any coin here is 1938. By tradition, the necklace should have stylised squash blossoms made of silver instead of the turquoise-mounted coins.

£3,000 — £4,000

Plate 258

Left to right, top to bottom

Aquamarine, paste and marcasite, octagonal shaped ring, c.1920.
£100 — £200

Rectangular chrysoprase, marcasite and silver ring, c.1920.
£100 — £200

Cornelian, marcasite and silver rectangular ring, c.1920.
£100 — £200

Square citrine ring, mounted with white sapphires.
£100 — £200

Art deco, synthetic sapphire and onyx ring in white gold.
£100 — £200

Art deco, 9ct. gold, carved coral ring.
£100 — £200

Oval onyx ring, set with diamonds in gold.
£100 — £200

Smoky quartz and green paste ring in silver.
£100 — £200

Green paste and marcasite ring in silver.
£100 — £200

Oval, lapis lazuli and 9ct. gold, signet ring.
£100 — £200

Synthetic ruby ring in gold mount.
£100 — £200

Onyx, silver and marcasite ring.
£100 — £200

Three stone, citrine ring surrounded with marcasites in silver.
£100 — £200

Jade and white gold oval ring.
£100 — £200

Synthetic ruby, marcasite, gold and silver mounted ring.
£100 — £200

Art deco, synthetic ruby, gold and white gold ring.
£100 — £200

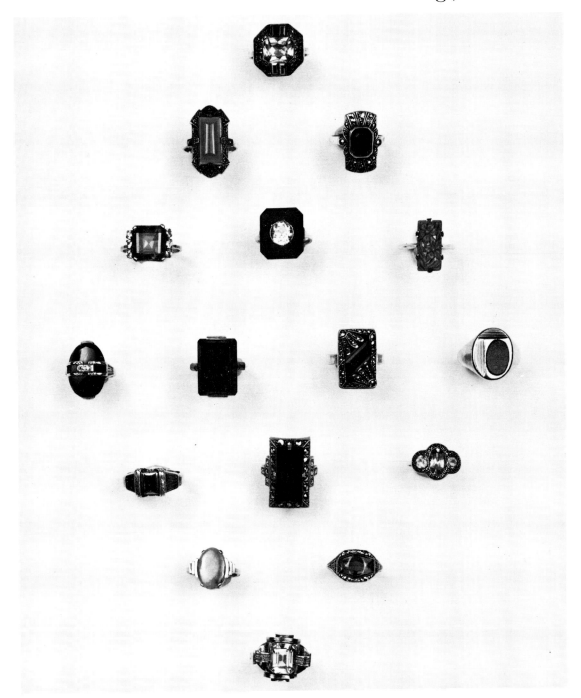

(Courtesy of Antiquarius, Bellamy, Tony & Sara, Thesaurus and The Purple Shop)

Plate 259

Left to right, top to bottom
Mid-18th century open design shoulders and carved shank.
Georgian, carved shoulders and shank.
Georgian, carved split-leaf shoulders, c.1830.
Georgian, decorative gold, lyre-shaped shoulders, c.1830.
Early Victorian, scrolled leaf shank and shoulders.
19th century, split-leaf shank on cluster head.
Mid-18th century, wide gold shank.
Enamel ring with plain gold band.
Early Victorian, scrolled shoulders, c.1840.
Mid-Victorian split shoulders, into three leaves.
Open shoulders with crowned claw setting.
Late Victorian, carved shoulders, c.1880.
Late Victorian, carved shoulders, c.1890.
Modern gold band, c.1900.

Side Views of Galleries
18th century, closed back setting, engraved on the inside of the shank.
18th century, silver, cut-down collet setting with engraved shoulders. Note the varying
height of the old-cut brilliants.
Mid-18th century, cut-down collet on a half-hoop ring, open-backed.
Mid-Victorian, half-hoop ring with a carved gallery and claw-setting.
Mid-Victorian, half-hoop ring with a carved gallery and claw-setting.
Late Victorian, crown claw mount.
20th century, traditional claw mount with plain shank. Note the difference in height
compared to 5 or 6.
Modern claw mount with plain shank.

(Richard Ogden)

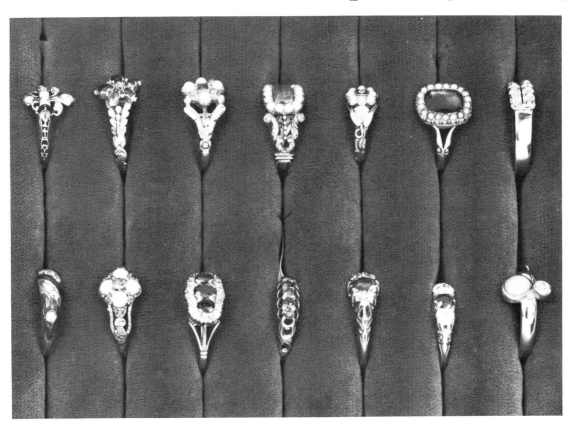

Plate 260

Left to right, top to bottom

Full eternity, set alternately with two emeralds and two diamonds. *£750 — £1,050*

Half eternity, set with emeralds and diamonds. *£450 — £650*

Half eternity, set alternately with two sapphires and two diamonds. *£500 — £600*

Full eternity, set alternately with three sapphires and three diamonds. *£600 — £750*

Half eternity, set alternately with three sapphires and three diamonds. *£450 — £650*

Half eternity, set alternately with sapphires and diamonds. *£600 — £700*

Full eternity, set with *calibré* cut sapphires. *£550 — £700*

Half eternity, set with brilliant-cut diamonds. *£650 — £900*

Full eternity, set with brilliant-cut diamonds. *£850 — £1,200*

Wide, half eternity ring, set with brilliant-cut diamonds. *£900 — £1,200*

Full eternity, set with brilliant-cut diamonds. *£1,000 — £1,300*

Full eternity, set with baguette diamonds. *£700 — £850*

Three row, full eternity, the diamond sections hinged to be worn either as a sapphire and diamond three row, or ruby and diamond. *£1,200 — £1,600*

Half eternity, set alternately with three rubies and three diamonds. *£900 — £1,000*

Half eternity, set with rubies and diamonds. *£700 — £850*

Full eternity, set alternately with three rubies and three diamonds. *£800 — £1,000*

Half eternity, set with rubies and diamonds. *£700 — £800*

Half eternity, set with rubies and diamonds. *£700 — £800*

Settings

Half eternity, solid gallery.

Full eternity, modern claw setting.

Half eternity with angular plain setting.

Full eternity with carved gallery.

Full eternity with plain setting.

Wedding Rings

18ct. gold , 8mm, blue enamel band.

18ct. gold, 6mm, 'Fabergé finish'.

18ct. gold 8mm, open-work circles, double row.

18ct. gold textured ovals.

18ct. yellow and white gold rectangles and squares.

18ct. gold twisted wire.

18ct. gold, four rows of yellow and white gold, twisted rope.

18ct. gold, three row, looped rope twist.

18ct. gold, white stippled band with yellow gold twisted rope.

18ct. white gold plait with frosted finish.

All £100 — £250

Signet Rings

Gold signet with seal-cut crest.

9ct. gold, oval signet with pale blue onyx centre.

9ct. gold signet, set with cushion-shaped lapis lazuli.

9ct. gold oval signet.

9ct. gold signet, set with cushion-shaped bloodstone.

9ct. gold, cushion-shaped signet.

9ct. gold, oval signet with textured gold mount.

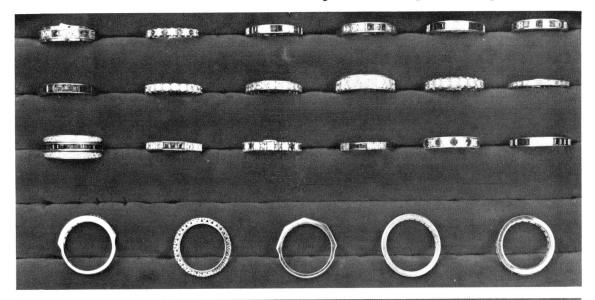

(Richard Ogden)

9ct. gold, oval signet, the textured mount with a bloodstone centre.
Ladies', 9ct. gold signet with lapis lazuli centre.
9ct. gold signet with broad head, matt finish.
9ct. gold signet with broad head.
All £75 — £280, plus any seal-engraving required.

Plate 261

Descending diagonally, left to right
Trap-cut amethyst, set as a ring in white gold with diamond shoulders.
£1,000 — £1,500
Mixed-cut amethyst, set as a ring in white gold with diamond shoulders.
£1,500 — £2,000
Oval, amethyst and diamond, cluster ring with 18ct. gold shank.
£650 — £1,000
Trap-cut aquamarine ring with diamond shoulders.
£2,000 — £2,500
Long trap-cut aquamarine ring with diamond shoulders.
£5,000
Oval, aquamarine and diamond, cluster ring.
£1,000 — £1,500
Brazilian topaz mounted as a ring in 18ct. gold.
£1,250 — £1,600
Green tourmaline ring with diamond trefoil shoulders.
£600 — £850
Peridot ring with diamond trefoil shoulders.
£1,200 — £1,400
Star sapphire ring, mounted in white gold with diamonds.
£1,000 — £1,500
Opal and diamond, half-hoop ring in carved gold setting.
£600 — £900

(Michael Poynder)

Plate 262

Read along pad, left to right, top to bottom
Large, diamond, cluster ring, claw set in yellow gold. £3,000 — £3,500
Diamond cluster ring in yellow gold. £1,800 — £2,500
Diamond cluster ring with diamond shoulders. £750 — £1,100
Floral, diamond cluster ring, in yellow gold. £700 — £900
Diamond cluster ring, plain shank. £475 — £675
Edwardian, diamond cluster ring in milled setting. £750 — £950
Traditional diamond cluster ring. £600 — £750
Spaced diamond cluster ring. £500 — £700
Diamond cluster ring with spaced outer stones. £600 — £800
Square shaped, diamond cluster ring. £500 — £600
Ten stone, diamond, half-hoop ring with white gold, twisted rope sides. £700 — £900
Five stone, diamond, half-hoop ring with white gold, twisted rope sides. £700 — £900
Traditional, five stone, diamond, graduated half-hoop ring. £600 — £800
Five stone, diamond, half-hoop ring, set in yellow gold. £600 — £800
Diamond and white gold, half-hoop ring, the diamonds set in diagonal bands of three.
£600 — £800
Diamond, double row, half-hoop ring. £600 — £800
Five stone, diamond ring in yellow gold. £450 — £550
Large, diamond, three stone ring. £3,000 — £4,000
Diamond, three stone ring in white gold. £1,200 — £1,500
Diamond, three stone ring with carved shoulders. £800 — £1,100
Diamond, three stone ring in white gold. £900 — £1,300
Graduated diamond, three stone ring in white gold. £1,000 — £1,500
Diamond three stone ring. £550 — £700
Diamond three stone ring, collet set. £500 — £700
Five diamond, three stone rings with slight variation in setting and price. £600 — £800
Gold ring, set diagonally with three diamonds. £375 — £500
Small diamond, three stone ring. £350 — £500
Square-cut diamond set as a ring with baguette shoulders. £1,400 — £2,100
Single stone, cushion-cut, diamond ring in open claw mount. £2,200 — £3,200
Trap-cut diamond ring with baguette diamonds on either side. £900 — £1,200
Single stone diamond ring. £500 — £650
Single stone diamond in heavy gold, claw mount. £650 — £850
Single stone, diamond ring in plain gold band. £500 — £650
Single stone, diamond ring in plain gold mount. £300 — £400
Single stone, diamond ring with engraved shoulders. £275 — £375
Single stone, diamond ring with baguette and small brilliants on the shoulders.
£850 — £1,200
Claw set, single stone, diamond ring. £350 — £450
Single stone, diamond ring set with four claws in a boat-shaped mount. £400 — £600
Single stone, diamond ring in gold. £350 — £450
Single stone diamond in a modern gold mount. £350 — £400 *(Richard Ogden)*

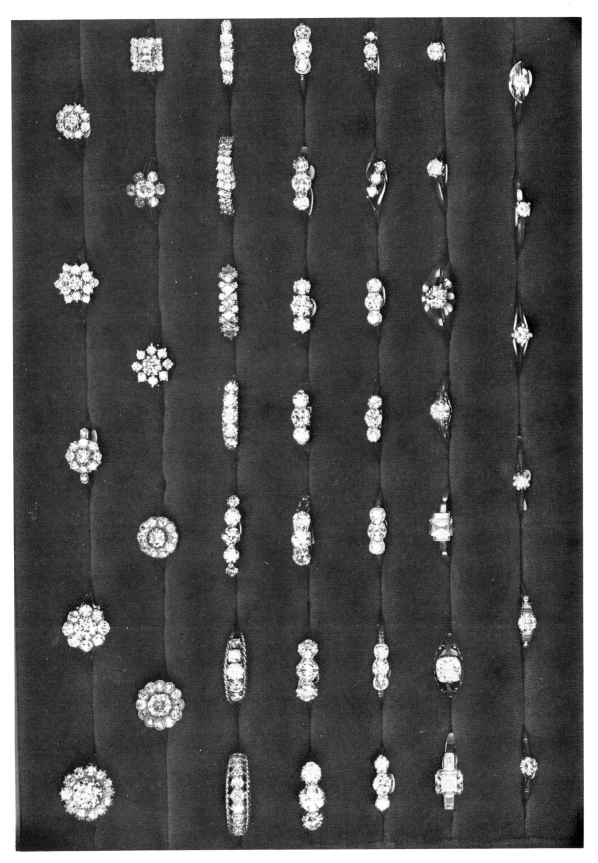

Plate 263

A range of 9ct. and 18ct. gold wedding rings, in white and yellow gold, the top half of the page are modern designs, cast in various patterns, the lower half of the page in traditional settings, from the Victorian era onwards, with plain, engraved or milled settings. The price varies largely according to carat, and the weight of gold contained in the ring. Most of the rings are made in 18ct. but some are available in 9ct.

£80 — £350

(Richard Ogden)

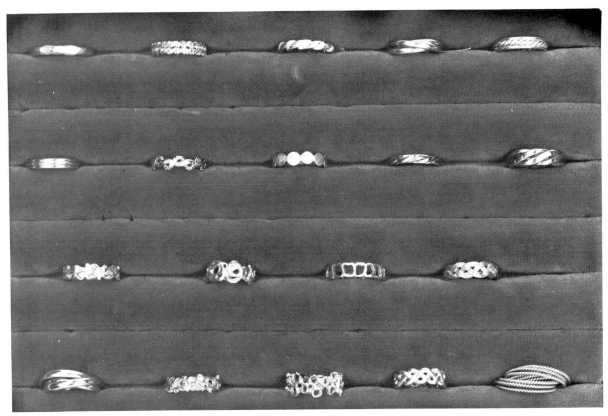

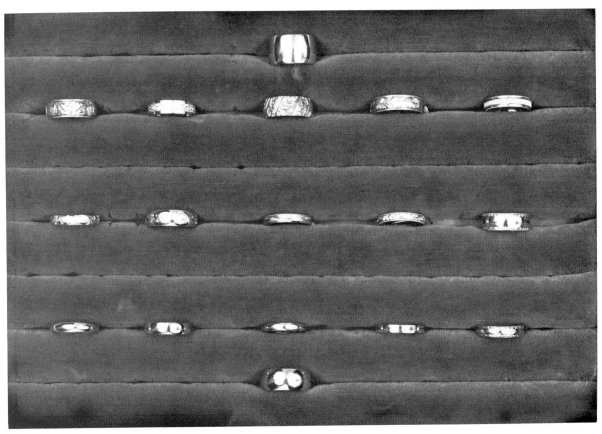

Lapis Lazuli

Lapis Lazuli, also known as lapis, derives from an old Persian word meaning blue, and the colour ranges from the deepest royal blue to pale greyish blue, speckled with white. It is an opaque rock rather than a true mineral.

Iron pyrites occurs in lapis lazuli and gives the effect of fine gold flecks in the stone. The best lapis is a deep royal blue of continuous even colour without any flecks of pale material. Powdered lapis was used by artists for centuries to produce the fine colours seen in Persian art and in Italian religious painting.

The major source of the best lapis is Afghanistan where it has been mined for over six thousand years, and the main area is the Badakshan region which is remote and inaccessible. The mines are at a great height, and it is only in recent years that they have been worked on a commercial basis. Other sources are South America (Andes), and Colorado, USA, but the quality is not as good. Surprisingly, the Mogok region of Upper Burma, best known for its rubies, also produces lapis.

Since lapis is opaque, there is little point in faceting it. In jewellery it is usually cut "en cabochon" or carved, particularly in Far Eastern jewellery. It is also cut as seals.

Technicalities: Chemical composition: aggregate of sodalite, hauynite, noselite and lazurite. Hardness: 5½. S.G.: 2.5-2.9. R.I.: 1.50. Since the finest lapis is valuable it is considered worth staining jasper blue to imitate it. This is known as "Swiss Lapis". Paste imitations containing spangles of copper crystals have also been made. Pale lapis itself has been stained a deeper blue, but this will wash out in time.

Marcasite

Marcasite jewellery dates from the middle of the 18th century and was a fashion which spread from France, where it was very popular at court. In this country most of it was made in Birmingham. The stones were rose-cut from the mineral iron pyrites and pavé set in silver, and sometimes in pewter. Marcasite jewellery was in vogue after the first and second world wars when it was hand set in die-cast silver mounts. A cheaper type was set with jeweller's glue in cast rhodium-plated base metal. Semi-precious stones, pastes and enamels are found in pieces made from the late 19th century onwards.

20th Century Marcasite and Paste Jewellery

Plate 264

Left to right, top to bottom
Silver and marcasite brooch of a dog, c.1940.
Silver basket of flowers brooch, set with cornelians and pastes, c.1940.
Silver, marcasite and coral pheasant brooch, c.1920.
Silver and paste, bar brooch of two monkeys, c.1940.
French multi-coloured paste and silver necklace, c.1925.
£60 — £200

(Antiquarius, Bellamy)

Cutting

Gemstones are either mined, or found in alluvial deposits. They occur as natural crystals and each species has its own particular crystal structure. The style of cutting stones has developed over the centuries in order to show the maximum amount of beauty from each stone — its colour, clarity, brilliance and shape.

Before the 16th century, diamonds were usually left in their natural octahedral shape (two four-sided pryamids base to base) and when set looked rather lifeless. The major source of diamonds in the old world was India, and with the opening of trade between Western Europe and the Orient in the 16th and 17th centuries the flow of diamonds and other gemstones from the East increased rapidly and new forms of cutting were devised. At this time, diamonds were flat-cut or table-cut, and coloured stones might be flat-cut or "en cabochon". However, this increase in the use of diamonds in Western jewellery brought about the rose-cut and the brilliant-cut, the latter being the most important and widely used form of cutting in all jewellery. The table-cut was developed into a form now known as the step, trap or emerald-cut, and this in turn has been combined with the brilliant to give the mixed-cut — a brilliant-cut crown and step-cut pavilion. In addition, other forms of cutting are used, including the marquise — in principle an elongated brilliant; pendeloque — a pear-shaped brilliant; briolette — a completely faceted drop bead; and baguette — a long trap-cut used for small diamonds in composite pieces of 20th century jewellery.

See diagrams on following pages.

Plate 265

1. Round, brilliant-cut diamond.
2. Marquise-cut diamond.
3. Trap-cut diamond (step-cut or emerald-cut).
4. Pear-shaped, brilliant-cut diamond.

The facets of the marquise and pear-shape are of modified proportions to the round brilliant, but follow the same basic design.

(De Beers Consolidated Mines Ltd.)

(De Beers Consolidated Mines Ltd.)

Plate 266

Examples of unmounted, circular, brilliant-cut diamonds, clearly showing the crown (and table facet), girdle and pavilion of a stone.

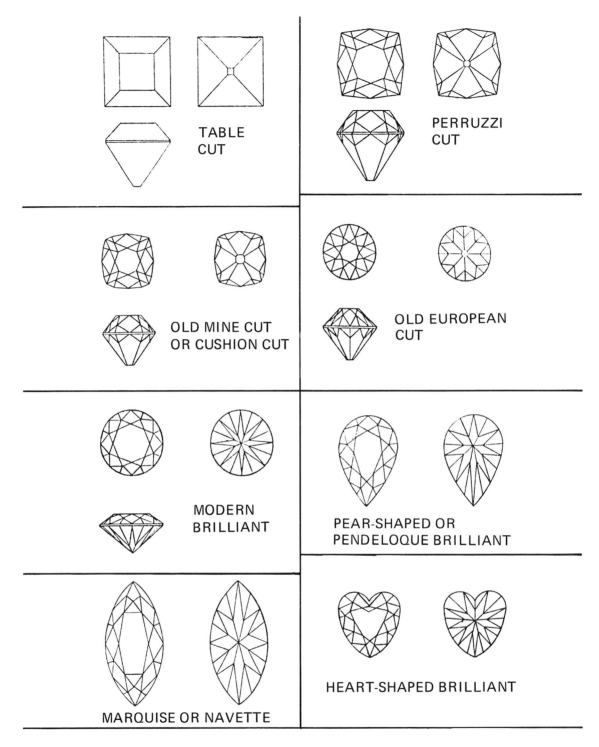

TABLE
CUT

PERRUZZI
CUT

OLD MINE CUT
OR CUSHION CUT

OLD EUROPEAN
CUT

MODERN
BRILLIANT

PEAR-SHAPED OR
PENDELOQUE BRILLIANT

MARQUISE OR NAVETTE

HEART-SHAPED BRILLIANT

(The diagrams on pages 342-344 are reproduced by kind permission of Mr. Eric Bruton from his book "Diamonds" published by Northwood Publications Ltd.)

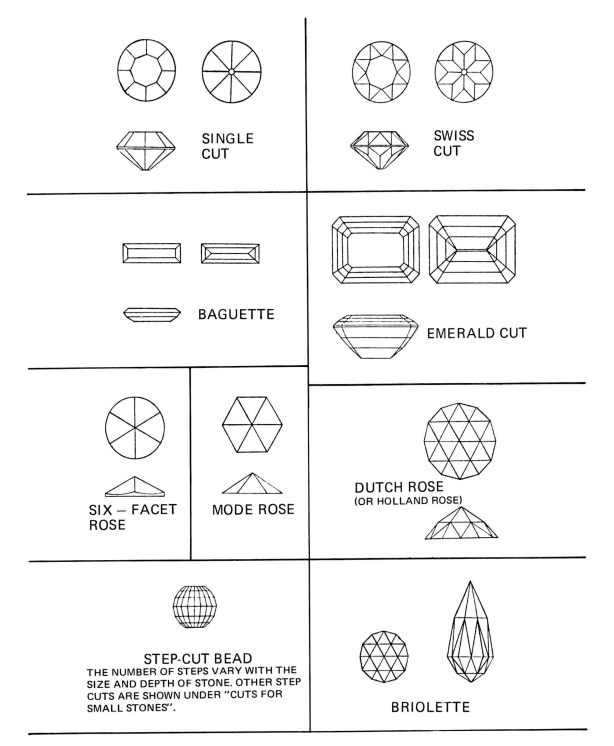

SINGLE CUT

SWISS CUT

BAGUETTE

EMERALD CUT

SIX — FACET ROSE

MODE ROSE

DUTCH ROSE
(OR HOLLAND ROSE)

STEP-CUT BEAD
THE NUMBER OF STEPS VARY WITH THE
SIZE AND DEPTH OF STONE. OTHER STEP
CUTS ARE SHOWN UNDER "CUTS FOR
SMALL STONES".

BRIOLETTE

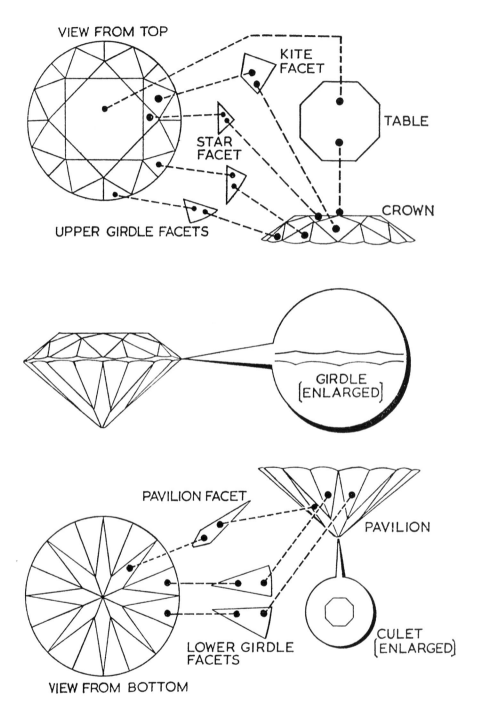

VIEW FROM TOP

KITE
FACET

TABLE

STAR
FACET

CROWN

UPPER GIRDLE FACETS

GIRDLE
[ENLARGED]

PAVILION FACET

PAVILION

LOWER GIRDLE
FACETS

CULET
[ENLARGED]

VIEW FROM BOTTOM

Parts of the brilliant cut diamond. The names of the facets have been simplified from the old cutters' terms and are generally accepted.

167

Mounting & Setting

Once a gemstone has been cut it is ready for setting in a mount — so that it can be worn. Within the jeweller's art there are many different individual crafts. For instance, the craftsman who cuts and polishes stones is called a lapidary but he would never make the mounts to take his stones. It is possible for a mounter — the craftsman who designs and cuts out mounts in metal — also to set the stones. But normally a mounter and setter are two different people performing two different crafts.

Mounting is the manufacture of metal cups or frames to hold gemstones so that they can be displayed or worn. The simplest and oldest form of mounting is a cup in which the stone is placed, the metal then being closed over the edge to hold it in. This is referred to as a "collet" and in this case is "closed backed". In early jewellery when the quality of stones often needed brightening, a layer of foil (tin foil, silver or coloured) was put in the collet before the stone was set. This is referred to as a "closed backed foiled collet".

The most important development from this was "claw" setting, which is self-explanatory. The number, shape and style of the claws, and craftsmanship dictate the beauty and simplicity of the finished article. Claw set stones are invariably "open backed", i.e. there is no metal behind the base of the stone. Hand made mounts are always better than cast mounts which are used in both antique and modern mass produced jewellery.

"Collet" and "claw" are two types of setting used in gem set jewellery and the many other forms of setting referred to in the book and listed below are only adaptations or embellishments of the two basic styles and are evident on the illustrations:

Collet (foiled or unfoiled)
Cut down collet
Closed back collet
Open backed collet
Claw
Claw with engraved gallery or mount
Claw with carved gallery or mount
Gypsy
Milled grain
Pavé
En tremblant
Filigree
Carmetille, etc.

The popular metals used in mounting through the centuries have been: electrum, gold, silver, copper, brass, iron, steel, platinum and various amalgams such as pinchbeck. The colours of gold can be varied by the inclusion of different base metals used to harden and strengthen pure gold, i.e.: white gold includes nickel; yellow gold includes brass; red gold includes copper, etc. All these metals were used extensively as they polish to a high degree and with the exception of steel are easy to work.

Plate 267

Left to right, top to bottom

Late Victorian, diamond ring brooch with cluster centre, open-backed and set in silver and gold.
£1,700 — £1,900

Victorian, carved moonstone head of a girl with a rose diamond-set bonnet in a closed silver setting, c.1860.
£1,200 — £1,500

Rose diamond-set, bar brooch designed as three birds on a branch, in a closed setting.
£450 — £500

Georgian, diamond, crescent brooch in a closed back setting, c.1800.
£1,800 — £2,200

Georgian, foiled brown topaz and half pearl cluster brooch, c.1820.
£450 — £500

Diamond daisy brooch with a pearl centre.
£600 — £700

Amethyst and rose diamond sunburst brooch, set in silver and gold, open-backed, c.1900.
£850 — £1,000

Victorian, pavé set, diamond bird with ruby eyes, open-backed.
£1,800 — £2,000

Blister pearl and diamond cockerel brooch, modern.
£850 — £1,000

Georgian, flat-cut garnet brooch-locket with hinged but empty centre compartment, the garnets foiled in a closed setting, c.1820.
£150 — £200

Late Victorian, Essex crystal and pearl pendant, normally closed back, but the back is missing in this case so that it is possible to see the method of reverse painting of the engraved crystal, c.1900.
£350 — £400

Late Georgian carbuncle, set as a brooch in a filigree gold setting with pearls and turquoises, c.1835.
£180 — £250

Early Victorian, *cannetille* work pendant, showing the coiling of the filigree gold into intricate patterns, forming a pendant/brooch, set with turquoises and pearls, c.1840.
£1,300 — £1,600

Mid-Victorian, gold bow brooch with a pendent heart locket, set with rubies and pearls, the gold background of the bow stippled to give it a textured look, and the heart engraved, c.1845.
£550 — £650

(B. Barnett Ltd.)

Front

Reverse

Plate 268

Enlargement of an early 18th century cross, set with table
and rose-cut diamonds, set in gold. Actual length 3½ins.
(8.4cm).

(Michael Poynder)

Plate 269

The reverse of a Victorian, diamond, flower spray brooch 'en tremblant', showing the coiled spring to allow independent movement of the flower head, c.1850. Although the front of the brooch is mounted in silver, the back is of gold to strengthen the framework. Actual length 2¾ins. (6.6cm). Mid-Victorian, rose diamond-set, fleur-de-lys pendant, set in silver and gold. The side view shows the claw setting of the centre diamond and the pierced gallery around the outside edge, c.1860. Actual height 2¼ins. (5.4cm).

Plate 270

Enlargement of a flat-cut garnet brooch in an 18th century mount, actual width of brooch
1⅜ins. (3.5cm).

Repairs

If people took more care of their jewellery and treated it with the respect and attention that hand-made work deserves, then they would not be continually paying out large sums of money for their own negligence. It is amazing that such valuable articles, with added sentiment and romantic attachment, can be treated so badly. Jewellery should be checked regularly for wear and tear. The following list covers the normal type of repair or break that occurs:

Rings

1. Shanks get thin on the palm side and will eventually break, probably causing the loss of the ring. A new half shank can be fitted at a fraction of the cost of the whole ring.
2. Galleries: close and constant contact with another ring will wear into a finely pierced gallery — which runs on either side of the body of a half-hoop or cluster rung — particularly when worn next to a wedding ring. This wear is acceptable and unavoidable as wedding rings and engagement rings are traditionally worn side by side, but eventually will necessitate remounting.
3. Claws will gradually rub down or break away if they are caught in strong synthetic fibre, such as nylon or terylene, which means that a valuable or sentimental stone could fall out. Re-tipping claws is expensive as the stone must be removed first, but it is necessary.
4. Rubbed stones: although a gemstone is hard, its surface will gradually scratch and chip until it becomes opaque and dull. This can be caused in a variety of ways: by knocking against other hard objects such as car doors, tables, etc., and also by keeping several hardstones jumbled together in a jewel box. However, a stone can easily be removed from its setting, repolished and reset.

Brooches

Brooches are usually lost due to faulty catches, or lack of safety catches and chains. These can be fitted at little extra cost, and are essential. If it does not matter which way up a brooch is worn, then it is safest to wear it with the pin pointing downwards, so that if the catch does come undone, the brooch will not fall out. Brooches are not normally damaged as easily as rings, but probably suffer more damage when put in a jewel box amongst other jewellery than when worn!

Necklaces and beads

1. Pearls and beads: regular restringing is obviously necessary and is usually left too late. Pearls are usually strong on silk and it is safer to have them strung knotted between each pearl so that if the silk breaks only one pearl will roll away and be lost. Pearls are regularly maltreated by being dropped on dressing-tables and scratched in jewellery boxes. They are not as hard as gemstones and will crack and chip easily. Women should always put on their pearls after their scent, as scent sprayed from an atomiser directly on to the pearls will eventually discolour them. Beads should be strung in the same way as pearls but with thicker silk.
2. Chains and links: chain links, be they gold or silver, will wear as they constantly rub together, and this cannot be prevented. To strengthen every link in a long-worn chain would be ridiculous, and when links finally become so thin that they break, it is time to replace the chain.

Foiled jewellery

Foiled jewellery should never be allowed to get wet, for if moisture gets behind the stone, the coloured, or silver, tinsel will discolour and the character of the brooch and the stones in it become dull and lifeless.

Seed pearl work

It is not fashionable today and very little remains in perfect condition since it is very fragile. Regrettably, if it does get broken, there are few jewellers capable or willing to take on this work. However, Messrs. E. & C. Austen of 207 High Holborn, London, WC1 are still prepared to try.

Enamel

Enamel is fragile and after all, only a form of glass, and therefore will chip, crack and scratch if it is allowed to be in contact with other stones. To touch up enamel is always a patchy job and will be noticeable to the trained eye. The alternative is to remove the enamel completely and start from scratch, but of course this is not practical with early jewellery as its character will inevitably be changed.

Cleaning

A little care and cleaning of your jewellery at home is not only worthwhile but rewarding — but please do not waste good gin! Any liquid or spirit that dissolves grease and dirt can be used in conjunction with a soft *bristle* toothbrush. Mix the spirit with whitening powder, working it into a stiff paste. Methylated Spirits is excellent for brightening metal. The powder should be brushed on to the jewellery and left to dry and then brushed off again. Goddards produce a ''Jewellery Care Kit'', which consists of a jar of special liquid, an immersible tray and a small stiff brush, and is ideal for cleaning jewellery at home, except, obviously, for foiled jewellery which must never be allowed to get wet. For cleaning the setting of the latter, dry whitening powder brushed over the metal with a soft bristle toothbrush will suffice without damaging the foil in any way.

Notes on repairs

Article	Date and Repair	Repairer	Cost	Remarks

The Beryl Family

The beryl family consists of a variety of attractive stones used in jewellery, the best known of these being emerald, which because of its importance, is treated separately. The other beryls are: aquamarine — sky-blue to pale green; morganite — pink; heliodor — yellow; and green beryl.

The Georgians and Victorians used pale greenish aquamarines mounted with gold in elaborate suites. At the turn of the century it was discovered that by treating aquamarines with controlled heat they turned sky-blue, and this type of stone is now fashionable and highly priced. Large aquamarines are usually mounted as single stone rings or pendants with baguette diamonds. Morganite is a soft pale pink, rather similar to pink sapphire or a pale tourmaline, but it is not widely used in jewellery. Heliodor, or golden beryl, has become more popular in recent years. Green beryl is found in 18th century jewellery, particularly Spanish and Portuguese, when it is often mounted with emeralds, or occasionally pastes and crystals. It tends to be a weakish green and is difficult to distinguish from pale emeralds without laboratory tests.

The main sources of aquamarine are Brazil and the Ural Mts. of Russia. (The fine aquamarine illustrated in the colour page of Fabergé jewellery — Plate 204 — is probably from the Russian mines.) Aquamarine is also found in the USA, Burma and Zimbabwe (Rhodesia), which all produce rather weak-coloured stones. Morganite is chiefly found in California and heliodor in Brazil, S.W. Africa and Madagascar. Green beryl is normally mined in the same locations as aquamarine.

As the various beryls tend to be pale it is important that the stones are fairly large when cut. They are normally trap-cut and set as rings, brooches and pendants, although stones in the centre of brooches are sometimes mixed-cut, and earrings, briolette-cut.

Technicalities: Chemical composition: beryllium aluminium silicate ($Be_3Al_2(SiO_3)_6$). Crystal structure: hexagonal forming six-sided prisms terminating in pyramids. Hardness: $7\frac{1}{2}$. S.G.: 2.68-2.90, aquamarines have lower density figure and morganites higher. R.I.: 1.57-1.59, again, aquamarines lower figure and morganites higher. Aquamarine is the only stone of the four mentioned which is of sufficient value to warrant imitation, and it is simulated by synthetic spinels and pastes.

353

Plate 271

A late, 18th century, Georgian basket of flowers brooch with various stones set in gold, actual
size 2ins. (4.8cm) high, enlarged to show details of setting.
Reverse shows where pewter has been used at the ends of the basket handle, and a patch which
has been put on at the base of the brooch fastening.

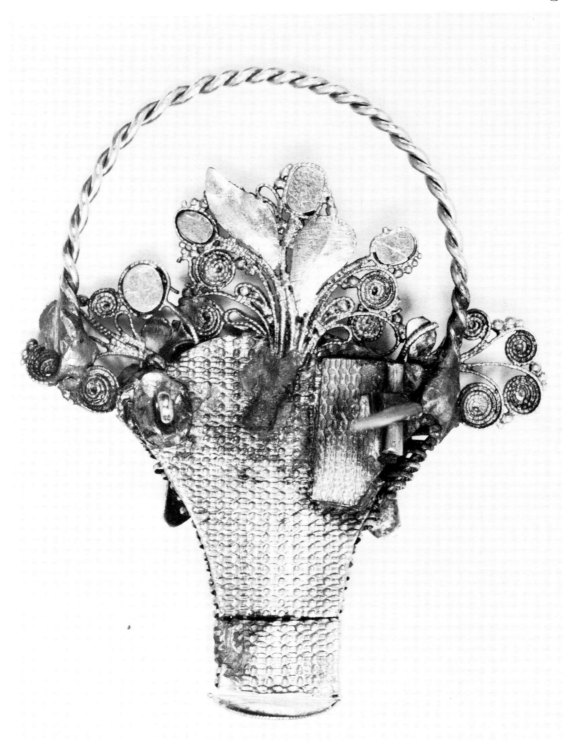

Reverse of Plate 271

The Jeweller's Tools

There are many sophisticated instruments available for identifying gemstones in the laboratory — high-powered microscopes, X-ray equipment, and so on. The working jeweller needs few tools other than his own experienced eye. In the normal course of his day's work he would expect to use: a diamond gauge, which doubles on the reverse as a pearl gauge; a 10× magnification lens; a magnifying eye-glass 2×, 4× or 6× to choice; a pair of jewellery tongs; a Moe's gauge, diamond weight calculator, consisting of a pair of calipers with a scale, and used in conjunction with a table; a Chelsea Colour Filter, which gives an indication of whether an emerald is genuine; and possibly, on occasion, a pair of hand scales.

With these tools an experienced jeweller can get by. When estimating the weight of stones other than brilliant-cut stones, he has to rely on experience and will usually be accurate to within a carat or two for larger specimens. However, when it comes to identifying individual stones, difficulties can arise as many stones appear to be similar. To tell the difference between a spinel, garnet, ruby and tourmaline — or deep pink sapphire — can be difficult. Equally well, the difference between precious topaz, citrine, yellow sapphire or zircon might cause confusion in some cases. Therefore, when jewellers are dealing with each other they will accept without question, and on trust, the seller's description of the stone on the understanding that if it proves to be other than described, it can be returned. A mistake is seldom made as when a jeweller buys a stone direct from a member of the public he will nearly always buy it subject to test, if it appears to be of sufficient importance. He will probably belong to the London Chamber of Commerce, whose gemmological section is second to none and whose opinion is universally accepted in the jewellery trade.

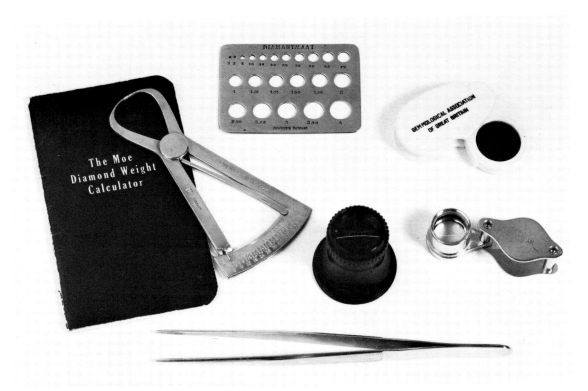

(Gemmological Instruments Ltd.)

Plate 272

Left to right, top to bottom
Moe diamond weight calculator.
Diamond gauge which doubles on the reverse as a pearl gauge.
Chelsea Colour Filter.
Jeweller's eyeglass.
Lens with a magnification of ten times.
A pair of stone tongs.

Registry Marks

The British Patent Office used this style of Registry Mark on British manufactured goods between 1842 and 1883. By knowing the code one can read the exact day, month and year when the article was registered. The letters were chosen at random, and starting in 1842 run as follows: X, H, C, A, I, F, U, S, V, P, D, Y, J, E, L, K, B, M, Z, R, O, G, N, W, Q, T. In 1868 the mark was changed fractionally, and followed the same sequence from X to K up to 1883 when this mark ceased and was replaced by numbers. The months were indicated by the following letters: C, G, W, H, E, M, I, R, D, B, K, A. R was used for 1-9 September 1857, K for December 1860, and G for 1-6 March 1868, the latter with W for the year.

From 1884 to 1900 serial numbers were used on registered designs. The first numbers in each year were as follows: 1884 — 1, 1885 — 19754, 1886 — 40480, 1887 — 64520, 1888 — 90483, 1889 — 11648, 1890 — 141273, 1891 — 163767, 1892 — 185713, 1893 — 205240, 1894 — 224720, 1895 — 246975, 1896 — 268392, 1897 — 291241, 1898 — 311658, 1899 — 331707, 1900 — 351202.

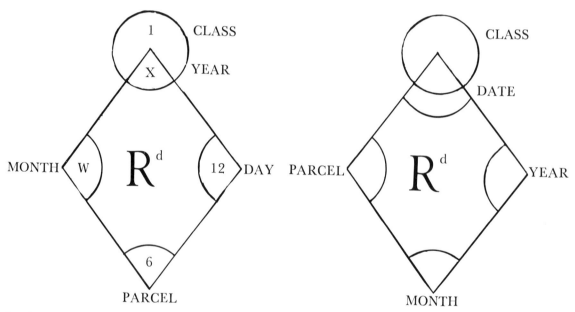

Registry mark used between 1842 and 1867.
Example is for 12th March 1842.

Registry mark for
1868-1883.

Plate 273

Enlargement of the British Registry Mark of the type used on manufactured goods between 1842 and 1883, this particular one is for 18th April 1871, taken from Plate 220 No. 3. See explanation of Registry Marks accompanying this photograph for further details.

Hallmarks

(Reproduced by kind permission of "The Assay Offices of Great Britain")

LOOK FOR THE HALLMARK ... it's your safeguard

British hallmarks have acted as a safeguard to purchasers of gold and silver articles for over six centuries. Hallmarking is still one of the most important forms of consumer protection and from 1st January 1975 (the effective date of the Hallmarking Act 1973) it is extended to include platinum for the first time. The consumer benefits in many ways under the new law. For example, it is an offence for any trader to sell or describe an article as gold, silver or platinum unless it has been hallmarked. (There are some exceptions, for example very small articles, certain specific items such as stone set gold rings and platinum articles if made before 1975, and all articles made before 1900.) The following questions and answers will help you to understand the hallmarking system.

Why do I need protection?

Pure gold, silver and platinum are too soft to be used in jewellery or domestic articles and are normally alloyed with other metals. This lowers the intrinsic value and also raises the question of how much other metal has been added. It is impossible to tell what proportion of precious metal there is in any article without the help of chemical analysis. Colour alone is no guide, even brass can look like gold — especially if it has been plated with gold.

How do hallmarks protect me?

Hallmarks on an article show that it has been tested at one of the official Assay Offices which are incorporated by royal charter or by statute and are independent of any trade organisation. They certify that the metal used conforms to one of the legal standards of fineness or purity. The analyses are extremely accurate and are carried out on small samples removed from the articles before they have been finally polished.

What information do hallmarks give?

The Sponsor's Mark

Indicates the manufacturer or sponsor of the article. The mark consists of the initials of the person or firm and where two or more sponsors have the same initials there is a variation in the surrounding shield or style of letters.

The Standard Mark

The present legal standards of gold, silver and platinum are as follows:

Gold	22 carat	916.6 parts gold in 1000 (or 22 in 24)
	18 carat	750 parts gold in 1000 (or 18 in 24)
	14 carat	585 parts gold in 1000 (or 14 in 24)
	9 carat	375 parts gold in 1000 (or 9 in 24)
Silver	Sterling	925 parts silver in 1000
	Britannia	958.4 parts silver in 1000
Platinum		950 parts platinum in 1000

The standard mark shows that the precious metal content of the alloy from which the article is made is not less than the standard indicated.

The Assay Office Mark

Identifies the particular office at which the article was tested and marked. There are now four Assay Offices — in London, Birmingham, Sheffield and Edinburgh. There were other Assay Offices in former times.

The Date Letter

Shows the year in which the article was hallmarked.

How can I recognise hallmarks?

Hallmarking was first instituted as long ago as 1300. The designs of individual marks have changed from time to time and new marks have been added. It is impossible to show all the hallmarks which you may come across, but the illustrations on the following pages should help you to identify some of them.

After 1st January 1975 all four Assay Offices use the same date letter. To date earlier pieces you will first have to identify the Assay Office mark before turning to the appropriate list. Date letters for the existing Assay Offices are given in this booklet. The marks shown are those used on silver. The same letters are used on gold but before 1975 the surrounding shields on gold may sometimes differ. Earlier cycles of letters and those for Assay Offices which have closed can be found in the more comprehensive publications. Here is an example of a complete hallmark.

It shows the sponsor's mark, followed by the mark for sterling silver, the London Assay Office mark and the date letter for 1975.

Standard Mark

British Articles

Prior to 1975	Standard	From 1975
[crown 22] / [22 thistle]	22 carat gold — Marked in England / Marked in Scotland	[crown] 916
[crown 18] / [18 anchor]	18 carat gold — Marked in England / Marked in Scotland	[crown] 750
[14] ·585	14 carat gold	[crown] 585
[9] ·375	9 carat gold	[crown] 375
[lion passant]	Sterling silver — Marked in England	[lion passant]
[thistle]	Marked in Scotland	[lion rampant]
[Britannia]	Britannia silver	[Britannia]
—	Platinum	[orb/crown pentagon]

Imported Articles

Prior to 1975	Standard	From 1975
[22] ·916	22 carat gold	916
[18] ·750	18 carat gold	750
[14] ·585	14 carat gold	585
[diamond] ·375	9 carat gold	375
925	Sterling silver	925
·9584	Britannia silver	958
—	Platinum	950

Assay Office Mark

British Articles

Prior to 1975		Assay Office	From 1975
[leopard's head] gold & Sterling silver	[lion's head] Britannia silver	London	[leopard's head] gold silver & platinum
[anchor] gold	[anchor] silver	Birmingham	[anchor] gold & platinum / [anchor] silver
[rose] gold	[crown] silver	Sheffield	[rose] gold & silver
[castle] gold & silver		Edinburgh	[castle] gold & silver

Notes — (i) Some variations in the surrounding shields are found before 1975. (ii) All Assay Offices mark Britannia silver, but only London (prior to 1975) had a special Assay Office mark for this standard.

Imported Articles

Prior to 1975		Assay Office	From 1975	
gold	silver		gold & silver	platinum
[Ω]	[Ω]	London	unchanged	[Ω]
[△]	[△]	Birmingham	unchanged	[△]
[Ω]	[Ω]	Sheffield	unchanged	—
[X]	[X]	Edinburgh	unchanged	—

OTHER MARKS

Here are some of the other marks which you may find on gold or silver articles.

Former Assay Office Marks

Several of the larger provincial cities had Assay Offices which are now closed. Each had its distinctive mark, some of the more important of which are shown below. There is also an Assay Office in Dublin and marks struck there before 1st April 1923 are recognised as approved British hallmarks. The Dublin mark is a figure of Hibernia.

Chester   Newcastle   Dublin   Glasgow   Exeter

Duty Marks

Between 1784 and 1890 an excise duty on gold and silver articles was collected by the Assay Offices and a mark depicting the Sovereign's head was struck to show that it had been paid. These are two examples.

George III   Victoria

Commemorative Marks

There have been two other marks to commemorate special events, the Silver Jubilee of King George V and Queen Mary in 1935 and the Coronation of Queen Elizabeth II in 1953.

Silver Jubilee Mark   Coronation Mark

Marking in Other Countries

Some countries besides Britain have hallmarking systems, but in many foreign countries the only marks used on precious metal articles are those struck by the manufacturer. These do not, of course, indicate the independent certification and consequent protection afforded by British hallmarks.

Further Reading

A study of hallmarks can become fascinating and rewarding. For anyone who wishes to learn more about hallmarks the publications listed below are recommended. Your local library should be able to provide books on the subject.

Bradbury's Book of Hallmarks. Published by J.W. Northend Ltd., Sheffield. (A handy pocket reference book.)

English Goldsmiths and their Marks by Sir Charles J. Jackson. Reprinted by Dover Publications Inc.

Further information may be obtained from: The Assay Office, Goldsmiths' Hall, Cutter Lane, London, EC2V 8AQ. The Assay Office, Newhall St., Birmingham, B3 1SB. The Assay Office, 137 Portobello St., Sheffield, S14DR. The Assay Office, 15 Queen St., Edinburgh, EH2 1JE.

Agates

Agates are a form of mineral quartz which occur under various well known names, depending upon the colour. They are generally translucent to opaque.

They are semi-precious and have been extensively used in jewellery, occurring in many cameos, seals and intaglios. They have always been popular and are still much used today, since they are colourful and inexpensive. Cornelian, the most common form of agate, is a light orange to deep and clear red. Bloodstone is a dark opaque green flecked with red. One of the rarer agates, chrysoprase, is an attractive translucent pale apple green. Pale varieties have been stained artificially to simulate the better greens, particularly favoured in Georgian and Victorian times. Onyx is a dark or reddish brown; this is often banded with white when it is referred to as sardonyx. It may also be stained black and is then known as black onyx. Jasper is either an opaque rich reddish brown or a pale bluish mauve; the two colours are sometimes found banded together and such stones were popular in signet rings. Agates may also be blue, green and translucent white; they sometimes contain inclusions of other materials which form in beautiful patterns, and can look like growing moss, bushes, trees or even landscapes. These are known as moss agates and were gut and mounted extensively in the late 18th and early 19th centuries, with borders of flat-cut garnets or with simple gold frames. Flat-cut plaques of the finest agates were used by the great snuffbox makers of this period, including Fabergé.

Australia produced many fine agates, although they are found worldwide. Scottish agates are still mounted today, when they are known as Scottish pebble jewellery. This jewellery, the finest of which was made in the Victorian era, is in the form of mosaics of various coloured agates, mounted in silver or gold. Moss agate occurs mainly in the Deccan region of India.

Agates are normally cut "en cabochon" or plaque-cut since, as already mentioned, they are extremely popular for engraving initials or cutting seals and intaglios. If they are evenly banded, they may be cut as cameos using layers in the design. However, in Victorian times, cheaper cameos cut from conch shells to achieve the same effect became more popular. Because they are not of sufficient quality, and they are nearly always opaque, agates are not normally faceted, except as beads.

Technicalities: Chemical composition: crypto-crystalline quartz (SiO_2). Crystal structure: trigonal, minute crystals. Hardness: 7. S.G.: 2.58-2.64. R.I.: 1.53-1.54. Agates are often stained; "Swiss lapis" and "Swiss jade" are both blue and green stained jasper.

Chrysoberyls

The chrysoberyl family consists of three stones, known as yellow chrysoberyl, a transparent greenish-yellow to brown, alexandrite, green in daylight, changing to red in artificial light, and cat's eye — the chatoyant variety of chrysoberyl.

Chrysoberyl is a hard, bright and attractive stone. In its transparent form it ranges from pale greenish yellow to brown, although the best known colour is yellow. Pale yellow chrysoberyls from Brazil were popular with the Spanish and Portuguese, and during the 18th century they were mounted in gold to form "chrysolite" jewellery.

The most valuable of the chrysoberyls is alexandrite, named after the Czar Alexander II, since it was first discovered in Russia in the 1830s. As mentioned above, alexandrite has a unique quality in that it changes from a grassy green colour in daylight, to a deep red under artificial light. Large alexandrites found in Sri Lanka, do not have such a strong colour change, the green appearing more grey, and the red more brown. Because of their rarity, alexandrites have been widely imitated.

Chrysoberyl cat's eyes are the best of their kind and the most highly priced. Their basic colour is greenish-yellow, with a sharp but milky cat's eye reflection across the stone. Quartz and tourmaline cat's eyes are not of the same colour or quality. The best specimens are found in Sri Lanka.

Chrysoberyls are usually flat-cut in Spanish and Portuguese jewellery, although they may be of mixed cut in the 19th century. Cat's eyes are cut "en cabochon" to show the chatoyant effect.

Technicalities: Chemical composition: a double oxide of aluminium ($BeAl_2O_4$). Crystal structure: orthorhombic. Hardness: 8½. S.G.: 3.71-3.72. R.I.: 1.75-1.76. Since alexandrite is rare and good pieces are very expensive, it has been imitated. Synthetic spinel and corundum have been made in the laboratory and show the colour change, although the colours are more subdued than in the natural alexandrite. They are sometimes sold as "synthetic" alexandrite and have led people to believe that they own a rare stone, whereas in fact the simulant is of little value.

Garnets

There are four types of garnet used in jewellery differing in colour from red to green. They are called pyrope, almandine, hessonite and demantoid.

Pyrope garnets: Sometimes called Bohemian garnets because of their traditional source in Southern Europe, they are a deep blood red colour, and were popular in Victorian jewellery. They are usually small in size and rose cut. Main source — Bohemia.

Almandine garnets: These are a lovely deep red, tinged with violet. Used in Greek, Roman and Anglo-Saxon jewellery, they were flat cut and set in brooches and pins, sword hilts and shields, as can be seen in the Sutton Hoo burial hoard in the British Museum. Almandines have been used extensively since then, in all forms. They were particularly popular in the late 18th and early 19th centuries, set in suites or as the surround for memorial and romantic brooches. Garnet jewellery was used by the middle classes of the period. In the Victorian era it was popular to cut almandines "en cabochon" and when cut in this way they are known as carbuncles. Main sources are India and Sri Lanka.

Hessonite garnets: They are bright orange-brown stones, not used as much as the other types of garnet, and often mistaken for sherry-coloured citrines or precious topaz. Main source — Sri Lanka.

Demantoid garnets: These are a bright vivid green with "fire" and are rarely found in excess of 5cts. The colour is something between an emerald and a peridot. The only source of any significance is the Ural Mountains of Russia and demantoids were first mined in any quantity in the latter part of the 19th century, therefore seldom appearing in antique jewellery prior to 1850.

Technicalities:

Pyrope: Chemical composition: magnesium aluminium silicate ($Mg_3Al_2(SiO_4)_3$). Crystal structure: cubic. Hardness: 7¼. S.G.: 3.80. R.I.: 1.75.

Almandine: Chemical composition: iron aluminium silicate ($Fe_3Al_2(SiO_4)_3$). Crystal structure: cubic. Hardness: 7½. S.G.: 3.95 and over. R.I. 1.78.

Hessonite: Chemical composition: calcium aluminium silicate ($Ca_3Al_2(SiO_4)_3$). Crystal structure: cubic. Hardness: 7¼. S.G.: 3.65. R.I.: 1.742-1.748.

Demantoid: Chemical composition: calcium iron silicate ($Ca_3Fe_2(SiO_4)_3$). Crystal structure: cubic. Hardness: 6½. S.G.: 3.82-3.85. R.I.: 1.89. Demantoid garnets have been imitated by paste, and a green, grossular garnet of the same composition as hessonite garnet has been used to imitate jade and is known as "Transvaal Jade".

Malachite

Malachite is a copper conglomerate, and a by-product of the copper-mines, hence its strong green colour. It varies in colour from a pale creamy green to an intense almost black green, usually colour-banded. These bands form attractive irregular curved patterns.

Because of its vivid colour, and the fact that it is found in large lumps, malachite has been used for objets d'art as well as in jewellery. It has been cut into fine flat pieces and used as a stone-veneer on ornamental pillars and vases, as in the Malachite Room at the Hermitage Museum, in Leningrad. It was used for the bodies of snuff-boxes and as an inlay for furniture by ébénistes, and for the cases of clocks, etc. Only the finest colours and forms were cut for use in 19th century mosaic jewellery where its unusual natural patterns can give shape and movement to a design.

The main source is the Ural Mountains of Russia, but it is also found in S. Australia, and, in particular, the Zaire copper-mines.

It is usually flat-cut for plaque brooches, or in small pieces for mosaic work, and cabochons and beads were popular in the late 19th century.

Technicalities: Chemical composition: hydrated copper carbonate ($Cu_2(OH)_2CO_3$). Crystal structure: monoclinic, usually minute crystals. Hardness: 4. S.G.: 3.8. R.I.: 1.85. Malachite is not hard, and can be broken and chipped quite easily.

Peridot

Peridot is a bright green stone, but of a different shade of green from any other stone, which could best be described as "oily". It belongs to the family known as olivine.

Peridot is classed as a semi-precious stone, although it is becoming rarer, and therefore more expensive. Fine specimens of unusually large size of the deeper green colour have been found in excess of 100cts., and there is a particularly beautiful example of 136cts. in the Geological Institute in London. They were popular in Victorian jewellery and it is possible to find necklaces of quite large stones set with diamonds.

The major source has traditionally been the Island of St. John in the south east end of the Red Sea, and peridots have also been found in the Mogok region of Upper Burma. Other sources are Hawaii, Australia, Norway, Brazil and Mexico. Peridot is normally trap-cut, although mixed cutting is not unusual.

Technicalities: Chemical composition: magnesium iron silicate $(MgFe)_2SiO_4$. Crystal structure: orthorhombic, frequently found as water-worn pebbles. Hardness: $6\frac{1}{2}$. S.G.: 3.34. R.I.: 1.65-1.68, with strong bi-refringence. The characteristic oily colour of peridot has been simulated in the laboratory by synthetic sapphire, and also by pastes.

Quartz

Quartz is the most common semi-precious stone used in jewellery. It has a wide colour-range, and forms in large clear crystals. Each colour has a different name: crystal or rock-crystal — colourless; citrine — yellow; smoky quartz — brown (in Scotland this is known as "Cairngorm"); amethyst — purple; rose quartz — pink; green quartz — green; and aventurine quartz — green, spangled with mica flakes.

Crystal has been used in jewellery from ancient times and together with white sapphires has imitated diamonds. Paste jewellery is regularly confused with crystal jewellery, as the two can look alike, although faceted and foiled crystals do have more life than paste. Clear crystals have been foiled with different colours to simulate various stones. Crystals may occasionally have inclusions of the mineral rutile which looks like short pieces of hair, and when red or golden-coloured, are known as "Venus hair-stone". Citrine is misnamed topaz, or quartz-topaz, and should not be confused with precious or Brazilian topaz. Citrines and smoky quartz were both popular in the 19th century. Amethysts have long been associated with the Church, as purple robes are strongly connected with Christianity. They have been used consistently in bishops' rings and crosses, and were also popular in Georgian, early Victorian and art nouveau jewellery. The finest amethysts are a rich purple showing red flashes of colour when turned in the light. Rose quartz is less common than other varieties and is seldom completely clear, usually having a milky look about it. Green quartz is not much used in jewellery. Another form of quartz, known as cat's eyes, are a greyish opaque colour with a whitish band of light. They are generally coarser than the fine chrysoberyl cat's eyes, but it is possible to confuse the two if the quartz cat's eye is of excellent quality. Crocidolite is asbestos which has been metamorphosed into quartz. It may be brown, blue or black. A whitish band of light across the base colour gives it the appearance of watered silk. Brown crocidolite is known as tiger's eye; blue and black as hawk's eye.

Quartz is found all over the world in large quantities and, when it occurs in clear crystals, it is worth cutting for use in jewellery. However, very large crystals, full of inclusions, also occur in all the colour ranges and have been cut and carved for ornamental purposes, i.e. Chinese snuff-bottles, bowls, gypsies' crystal balls, German Renaissance crystal carvings, etc. Citrines come from Brazil and smoky quartz from Scotland and Manchuria. The finest amethysts are found in Siberia and Madagascar. Rose quartz is largely found in Brazil, aventurine quartz in India, crocidolite in Africa and quartz cat's eyes in Sri Lanka.

Quartz is cut in most of the different styles, and the quartz cat's eyes are naturally cut "en cabochon" to show the chatoyancy. Crocidolite may be plaque cut or "en cabochon". Quartz beads are common, and may be faceted or rounded.

Technicalities: Chemical composition: silicon dioxide (SiO_2). Crystal structure: trigonal, forming prisms with pyramids. Hardness: 7. S.G.: 2.65. R.I.: 1.54. Amethyst may be treated with heat to turn it yellow. Clear quartz is often used in doublets and triplets to imitate emerald, or as the top layer of an opal triplet.

Spinel

Spinel is normally found as a red stone, although it does occur in light and dark blue, green and black.

Red spinel is known as "Balas Ruby" and is infamous in that it is often mistaken for, and passed off as ruby, since it is found in the same areas in S.E.Asia. Its colour range is similar to ruby, although it can never be compared to the "pigeon's blood" Burma rubies, and is found in much larger sizes. One of the best-known spinels must be "The Black Prince's ruby" in the Imperial State Crown. Pale blue spinel, which is not a particularly expensive stone, is used to imitate aquamarine, but can be identified as it is a considerably denser stone. Spinels are not much used in Western jewellery today, but occur frequently in asiatic jewellery in conjunction with coloured sapphires.

The principal sources are Sir Lanka and S.E. Asia. They are usually trap, step or mixed cut when meant to simulate other stones.

Technicalities: Chemical composition: magnesium aluminate ($MgAl_2O_4$). Crystal structure: cubic. Hardness: 8. S.G.: 3.58-3.90. R.I.: 1.71-1.74. Spinels are synthesised in the laboratory, particularly colourless ones used to imitate diamonds.

Topaz

Topaz is a gem species in its own right, and two different colours of topaz are used in jewellery: yellow-brown, which is known as "Brazilian" or "precious", and pink. Yellow citrine (quartz) is sometimes wrongly called topaz, or quartz-topaz, but it is a completely different stone.

The beautiful sherry-coloured topaz is hard and polishes well, giving it a bright appearance. It is transparent and usually of even colour, but is easily fractured, so it must be treated with care. Precious topaz was popular with the Georgians and Victorians, probably because it was found in Brazil in the 18th century, and is frequently set in foiled settings with pearls. Pink topaz is rare as a natural stone and the colour is more often induced by heating the sherry-brown stones until they change to pink. However, it is used in Georgian jewellery, usually mounted in a closed setting and backed with pink foil to heighten the colour.

Because topaz is formed in long crystals, it is often cut as a long thin stone, sometimes trap-cut, but more usually mixed-cut, as this shows off its brightness to advantage.

Technicalities: Chemical composition: a fluosilicate of aluminium $(Al_2(F,OH_2)_2SiO_4)$. Crystal structure: orthorhombic. Hardness: 8. S.G.: 3.53. R.I.: 1.63-1.64.

Tourmaline

Tourmaline is a stone with a wide variety of colours. Apart from its interest to jewellers, it is used widely in the scientific field, since it will conduct electricity. In jewellery it is best known for its fine pinkish red stones, sometimes called rubellite, which can command quite high prices and occur in large sizes. Dark green tourmalines are becoming more popular. Blue tourmalines are occasionally found in jewellery, although they are not common. Some modern jewellery makes use of the whole natural tourmaline crystal, which is found divided between the pink and green colours, in one crystal, and forms an unusual colour combination.

Tourmaline was probably introduced to Europe from Sri Lanka in the early 18th century. It is found all over the world but the better stones come from Russia, Burma (Mogok area produces fine rubellites), Sri Lanka, Brazil, Madagascar and California. S.W. Africa produces a bright green tourmaline called "chrome tourmaline" because it is coloured by chromium.

The mixed-cut is normal, although step-cutting is used for the better stones. Tourmaline may also be carved, with geometric or floral designs on pieces of lesser quality which are not clear enough to facet or cut as beads.

Technicalities: Chemical composition: a complex borosilicate of aluminium and alkalies with iron, magnesium, calcium, manganese, lithium, potassium, fluorine and water. Crystal structure: trigonal. Hardness: 7¼. S.G.: 3.01-3.06. R.I.: 1.62-1.64. Because tourmaline can create an electrical charge, when it is heated, as in a shop window, it will attract dust and look dirty.

Turquoise

Turquoise is a stone which can vary in colour from the blue described by its own name to a palish blue-green, and it is opaque.

It was used a great deal in early Egyptian and Persian jewellery in conjunction with coral and gold. Later it became popular with the Victorians and may be found in fine suites of jewellery, often in conjunction with pearls. The best turquoise is a bright blue, but the poorer varieties tend to be greenish and contain flecks and seams of the natural parent rock, which is known as limonite. Turquoise is porous and may discolour after a time from the acids absorbed from the human skin. Scent will also cause discoloration.

Iran, the Sinai Peninsula, Tibet, India and China are all major sources. Turquoise is also found in Mexico where it was used in Aztec jewellery, and in Colorado and New Mexico where with silver it became the traditional jewellery of the Indian tribes. Russia is another source and turquoise has surprisingly been found in Cornwall, but of poor quality.

The best material is cut "en cabochon", although it may be faceted. It is frequently pavé set. Larger pieces make fine hardstone ornaments.

Technicalities: chemical composition: hydrous copper aluminium phosphate. Crystal structure: triclinic, although in most cases crypto-crystalline. Hardness: 6. S.G.: 2.60-2.90. R.I. 1.61-1.65. Since the finest turquoise is valuable, it has been imitated by stained ivory, porcelain, vitreous glass and enamel. All of these can be recognised by the experienced eye. Turquoise itself is sometimes stained in order to improve the colour, but this colour is often only superficial and will reveal itself if the stone is cut or scratched.

Zircons

Zircons are semi-precious stones which in natural form are usually a dull green or brown colour. When heated, they become white, golden yellow or blue stones.

They have a high refraction which gives them a brilliant appearance, and for centuries the white stones have been used to imitate diamonds in Asiatic and Middle Eastern jewellery. White sapphires are used in the same way and both are referred to as jargoons. The most common zircon in Western jewellery is the blue stone, the colour having been induced artificially by heat treatment. These stones, when set with diamonds, were popular in jewellery of the 1930s and 1940s. When red, orange and brown zircons occur naturally, they are known as jacinths. Zircons are not a particularly popular stone in the West today, but are still used a great deal in cheap Eastern jewellery.

The principal sources are Burma, Thailand and Sri Lanka.

In Eastern jewellery, jargoons are flat or rose-cut, backed with foil and usually set in gold. In the West, they are nearly always brilliant-cut to show their "fire" at its maximum.

Technicalities: Chemical composition: zirconium silicate ($ZrSiO_4$). Crystal structure: tetragonal. Hardness: 7-7½. S.G.: 4-4.70. R.I.: 1.92-1.98, with strong bi-refringence in some cases.

Explanation of Technical Terms for Identification of Stones

Chemical Composition: The chemical make-up of each individual stone, and formula.

Crystal Structure: Gemstones fall into one of seven categories of crystal formation which are referred to as follows, beginning with the most perfect and symmetrical: cubic, tetragonal, orthorhombic, hexagonal, trigonal, monoclinic and triclinic. In some cases, stones are referred to as micro-crystalline, or crypto-crystalline, and they are formed by minute crystals packed tightly together. These are opaque stones and normally porous, and they can be stained to improve the colour, e.g. some agates, lapis lazuli and jade. Stones may also be amorphous, i.e. with no identifiable crystal structure.

Hardness: Hardness in gemstones is defined by a scale known as Mohs scale, calculated in 1822 by Friedrich Mohs. He chose ten representative stones and minerals to form the scale, beginning with the hardest substance, diamond, which he graded 10, descending through corundum — 9, topaz — 8, quartz — 7, feldspar — 6, apatite — 5, fluorspar — 4, calcite — 3, gypsum — 2, to talc — 1. Glass varies from 4 to 6, according to its lead content, and steel rates around 6. The scale is uneven and the gap between 9 and 10 is, for instance, much greater than from 8 to 9. Therefore it can only be used as a comparison of hardness from one stone to another, rather than as a regular linear scale. As far as identification is concerned, it is useful in conjunction with other tests, and will give immediate identification of, for example, a diamond, from its simulants, e.g. white sapphire (9), white spinel (8) or strontium titanate (6½).

Specific Gravity: Specific gravity means the density or "heaviness" of an article. A scale has been devised to measure the density of objects and is based on the density of water which is taken to be 1. Equivalent volumes of water and stones are compared and the difference in weight will be the specific gravity figure expressed. Therefore, a stone such as a diamond, with an S.G. of 3.52 will be 3.52 times as dense as the same volume of water. Specific gravity is particularly useful in identifying different gemstones, as every species has its own density and will help to tell the difference between two stones which appear to be of the same family.

Refractive Index: When light rays enter a stone they appear to bend. This bending, or refraction of light, happens whenever light passes from one medium to another. This can easily be noticed if a person is observed standing in water up to his waist. His legs will appear to be much shorter than in real life because water refracts light at a different rate from air. Every gemstone will refract light at a different angle and a scale, known as the Refractive Index, expresses this numerically in order to help identification of the stones. Air is considered as 1, and the proportion of the bending of the light ray when it enters the stone expresses the stone's refractive index. It is measured on a refractometer, and together with specific gravity forms a combination of figures, so that two different types of stone will rarely coincide. A refractometer can only be used with cut stones and is an essential part of a jeweller's equipment.

Weights and Measures

Rough or cut stones are weighed in carats:

$$1 \text{ carat} = \frac{1}{5} \text{ or } .200 \text{ grammes}$$
$$1 \text{ diamond or pearl grain} = \frac{1}{4} \text{ or } .250 \text{ of a carat}$$

A diamond weighing less than a carat is referred to as having so many points which is the percentage expression, i.e. a ¾ carat diamond is referred to as being 75 points.

Pearls are referred to in grains: 1 grain = ¼ of a carat. However, unlike diamonds, pearls are never referred to as being of so many points if less than a carat.

Metric weight is the expression of grammes:

$$1000 \text{ milligrammes} = 1 \text{ gramme}$$
$$1000 \text{ grammes} = 1 \text{ kilo}$$
$$1 \text{ gramme} = 5 \text{ carats}$$
$$500 \text{ milligrammes} = 2\frac{1}{2} \text{ carats, etc.}$$

The Troy weight scale is often used in the jewellery, gold and silver trade:

$$24 \text{ grains} = 1 \text{ pennyweight (dwt)}$$
$$20 \text{ dwts} = 1 \text{ ounce (oz)}$$
$$12 \text{ oz} = 1 \text{ pound (lb)}$$

However, the normal domestic Avoirdupois scale is also used, the scale learnt in the schoolroom:

$$16 \text{ drams} = 1 \text{ ounce}$$
$$16 \text{ oz} = 1 \text{ lb}$$
$$14 \text{ lbs} = 1 \text{ stone}$$

It is therefore vital to know which scale you are using when weighing gold etc., on a spring balance. Here is the conversion between the various scales, which is enough to confuse anyone, but necessary to have available:

Grains to grammes	×	0.0648
Grammes to grains	×	15.4324
Pennyweights to grammes	×	1.5552
Grammes to pennyweights	×	0.6430
Ounces (Troy) to grammes	×	31.1035
Grammes to ounces (Troy)	×	0.03215
Ounces (Troy) to ounces (Avoirdupois)	×	1.09714
Ounces (Avoirdupois) to ounces (Troy)	×	0.91146
Ounces (Avoirdupois) to grammes	×	28.3495
Grammes to ounces (Avoirdupois)	×	0.03527
Pounds (Avoirdupois) to ounces (Troy)	×	14.5833
Ounces (Troy) to metric carats	×	155.517
Ounces (Avoirdupois) to metric carats	×	141.7475
Pennyweights to metric carats	×	7.77
Inches to milimetres	×	25.400
Inches to centimetres	×	2.540

Birthstones Relating to the Signs of the Zodiac

Many different versions are given and this list amalgamates some of them: the leading sign of the Zodiac is considered to be Aries.

Aries	March 21 — April 20	Diamond
Taurus	April 21 — May 20	Emerald and Coral
Gemini	May 21 — June 20	Pearl and Agate
Cancer	June 21 — July 21	Ruby and Moonstone
Leo	July 22 — August 21	Peridot and Amber
Virgo	August 22 — September 21	Sapphire and Jade
Libra	September 22 — October 22	Opal and Lapis Lazuli
Scorpio	October 23 — November 21	Topaz and Bloodstone
Sagittarius	November 22 — December 20	Turquoise
Capricorn	December 21 — January 19	Garnet and Malachite
Aquarius	January 20 — February 18	Amethyst and Jacinth
Pisces	February 19 — March 20	Aquamarine

Glossary

ADULARESCENCE: Term applied to the milky sheen in moonstones.

AGGREGATES: Minerals which form without showing their outer crystal shape.

AIGRETTE: Hair ornament.

ALBERT: Watch-chain.

ALEXANDRITE: Type of chrysoberyl, green in daylight and red in artificial light.

ALMANDINE: Purplish-red variety of garnet.

AMAZONITE: Opaque, blue and white coloured feldspar.

AMBROID: Small pieces of amber pressed together.

AMETHYST: Purple quartz.

AMORPHOUS: Without any crystal form.

ANGEL SKIN: Pale pink coral.

AQUAMARINE: Pale blue/green beryl.

ASTERISM: Term applied to the star effect seen in some stones, also known as "star stones", e.g. star sapphire.

AVENTURINE GLASS: Artificial spangled glass, made to imitate green and golden aventurine quartz, and when golden in colour is known as "goldstone".

BAGUETTE: Elongated rectangular cut diamond.

BAKELITE: An artificial resin or plastic dyed in various colours to imitate natural stones.

BALAS RUBY: A term for red spinel, dating back to the Middle Ages.

BAROQUE: Refers to pearls of irregular form.

BASSE TAILLE: Form of engraving rays and two-dimensional designs into the back plate and building up the enamel in translucent layers to produce a shimmering effect.

BI-REFRINGENCE: The splitting of refracted light into two rays which give different readings on a refractometer. All crystals except those of the cubic system are bi-refringent and a measure of a stone's bi-refringence is helpful in identification.

BLISTER: Pearls which form in semi-circular shape, attached to the mantle of the oyster.

BLOODSTONE: Dark green variety of chalcedony (agate), speckled with red jasper.

BOG OAK: Black oak, preserved in peat, used in Victorian mourning jewellery.

BOWENITE: Yellowish-green form of the aggregate "serpentine", sometimes confused with jade.

BRILLIANT-CUT: Form of diamond cutting with 58 facets.

BRIOLETTE: Form of cutting used for drop-shaped stones.

CABOCHON: Dome-shaped cut used for opaque and star-stones, and also for precious stones of lesser quality.

CAIRNGORM: Name given to the clear brown or "smoky" quartz crystals found in the Cairngorms in Scotland and used in Scottish jewellery.

CAMEO: Form of cutting in relief, used particularly with agates and shells where the colour banding is incorporated in the carved design.

CANNETILLE: Form of filigree gold-work used in late 18th and early 19th century jewellery.

CARAT: 1) Method of describing the weight of stones. 5cts. = 1gm. 2) Ratio of precious metal to its alloys, divided into parts of 24, i.e. 18ct. gold is ⅔ gold, ⅓ alloy, and anything of 22cts. and over is considered to be "fine" or pure gold.

CARBUNCLE: Cabochon-cut almandine garnet (deep purplish-red colour).

CAT'S EYE: Chatoyant variety of chrysoberyl. Other varieties of stones produce cat's eyes, but are normally prefixed by their particular species, e.g. quartz cat's eyes.

CHAMPLEVÉ: Early type of enamelling where different coloured molten enamel is poured into hollowed-out sections of the metal design.

CHATELAINE: Attachment to a lady's belt from which hung useful objects such as keys, scissors, thimble, etc.

CHATOYANCY: Term applied to the sharp band of whitish light which is reflected from the surface of some stones when cut "en cabochon".

CHELSEA COLOUR FILTER: Filter used for identifying certain gemstones, particularly emeralds.

CHRYSOLITE: Name given to pale yellow chrysoberyls, frequently used in 18th century Spanish and Portuguese jewellery.

CHRYSOPRASE: Pale green translucent variety of chalcedony (agate).

CITRINE: Yellow variety of quartz.

CLASSICAL: Should refer to the Greek and Roman eras, sometimes used loosely to denote "in the classical style" when referring to 18th and 19th century craftsmanship.

CLEAN: Stones without any flaws visible under a 10× lens.

CLOISONNE: Early type of enamelling where the design is formed by soldering metal thread to a metal plate, and the enamel is then applied and polished flat.

CLOSED BACK: Jewellery which is set with stones in "cups" of metal so that the reverse of the stone is not visible. Stones in closed settings are backed with a layer of coloured foil or painted in order to heighten the colour.

CORNELIAN: Translucent orange variety of chalcedony (agate).

CORSAGE: Jewellery attached to the bodice of a dress, generally fairly large pieces.

CORUNDUM: Gem species of rubies and sapphires.

CROCIDOLITE: Asbestos which has been fossilised into quartz.

CROWN: Top half of a brilliant-cut stone, i.e. the part above the "girdle".

CRYSTAL: A piece of material whose atomic structure is reflected in its outer form, which for definition purposes has been divided into one of seven different "crystal systems" according to its regularity.

CULET: The bottom facet of a brilliant-cut stone.

CUSHION-CUT: Old form of brilliant-cut, developed in the late 17th century by Peruzzi in Venice.

DEAD PAWN: Unclaimed pieces of American Indian jewellery.

DEMANTOID: Bright grass-green coloured garnet.

DOUBLET: Two pieces of stone stuck together in imitation of pieces of better quality or size. In the case of opal, a thin piece of precious opal is backed with opal matrix. Doublets may be "true doublets", i.e. they are made of the natural stone, or they may be simulants, or even a mixture of both.

ELECTRUM: A natural alloy of gold and silver, used by the Greeks.

EMERALD-CUT: Another term for step- or trap-cut.

EROTES: Greek name for cherubs.

ESSENCE D'ORIENT: Substance made from fish-scales used for coating artificial pearls, simulating the lustre of nacre.

ESSEX CRYSTAL: Rock crystal, cut "en cabochon" with a design engraved and painted on the reverse, popular in the Victorian era.

FANCY-COLOURED: Any colour in a stone other than its expected normal colour, e.g. sapphires other than "blue" and diamonds other than "white".

FELDSPAR: Gem family, best known in jewellery as moonstones, sunstones, labradorite and amazonite.

FILIGREE: Metal work formed of fine wires twisted into ornate patterns.

FLAT-CUT: Form of cutting a tablet of stone with a large flat top surface.

FAIENCE: Glazed earthenware, also used for making beads, scarabs, etc. from the Egyptian period onwards.

FLORENTINE WORK: Form of inlay in jewellery using sections of differently coloured hardstone and ivory to create designs.

FOILING: See **CLOSED BACK.**

FOSSILISED: Objects which have been turned to stone, sometimes used in jewellery, e.g. petrified wood.

FRENCH JET: Black glass jewellery imitating jet.

GIRANDOLE: A popular 18th century design of jewellery with swinging pear-shaped drops on pendants, brooches and earrings.

GIRDLE: Widest part of a brilliant-cut stone, between the crown and the pavilion, usually partly hidden when the stone is set.

GOLDSTONE: Gold-spangled glass imitating aventurine quartz.

GROSSULAR GARNET: Type of garnet, the green variety of which is used to simulate jade, known as "Transvaal jade".

GUTTA PERCHA: Glutinous resin from trees, used by Indian craftsmen in the manufacture of jewellery.

GYPSY-SET: Stones set deeply into the metal mount.

HARDSTONE: Normally applied to decorative opaque stones used for inlay work or cameos, e.g. lapis lazuli, agates, jades.

HALLEY'S COMET: Comet which appears every 76 years, named after Halley in 1759 following its appearance in 1758. It was recorded in 1834 and 1910 and jewellery in the form of a comet was made, particularly in 1834 in commemoration.

HEAT TREATMENT: Some stones when heated change colour or deepen their existing colour which makes them more attractive, and more saleable.

HELIODOR: Golden-coloured beryl.

HOLBEINESQUE: 19th century jewellery in the Renaissance style, after Holbein.

IMITATION: One material simulating another of different substance.

IMPERIAL JADE: Highly prized jadeite of a brilliant translucent green.

INCLUSIONS: Faults in the natural crystal which may take the form of gas bubbles, liquid-filled cavities or small crystals, which help to identify the type and source of the stone.

INTAGLIO: Cutting into a stone, the reverse of cameo cutting.

IRIDESCENCE: Shimmering effect of rainbow-like colours which will change with the light, e.g. opals, labradorite, butterflies' wings and oil all show iridescence.

IVORINE: Plastic or Bakelite simulating ivory.

JACINTHS: Yellow, orange and red zircons, sometimes also called hyacinths.

JADEITE: Greenish opaque stone varying from a brilliant translucent green to white, usually known as "jade" and confused with nephrite, which is generally less valuable and varies in colour.

JARGOON: Name for white sapphires and white zircons in Indian jewellery, a term sometimes incorrectly applied to rose-cut diamonds.

JASPER: A form of agate, an opaque rusty red colour.

LABRADORITE: Type of feldspar first found in Labrador, exhibiting bluish-green iridescence on a grey background, popular in art nouveau jewellery.

LAVA: Light, porous volcanic material carved and set in 19th century jewellery.

LIGNUM VITAE: A particularly hard wood.

LIMOGES ENAMEL: Enamels painted in "grisaille", perfected at Limoges, often taking the form of portrait enamels in the Renaissance style.

MABE PEARLS: The cultured pearl version of blister pearls. The hollow semi-circular pearl is filled with wax and backed with mother-of-pearl. Mabé means "half" in Japanese.

MADEIRA CITRINE: Deep brownish-orange coloured citrine.

MATRIX: Parent rock in which the gemstone is found, occasionally incorporated in pieces of jewellery, particularly with carved turquoise and opal.

MEMENTO MORI: Literally "Memory of the Dead". Applied to Medieval and Renaissance memorial jewellery.

METAMORPHOSIS: The changing of one substance into another, associated with volcanic activity on pre-existing rocks or materials, e.g. asbestos fibres underwent metamorphosis to become crocidolite.

MILLED: Type of setting popular in Edwardian jewellery, also known as *millegrain*.

MIXED-CUT: Brilliant-cut crown and step-cut pavilion of a stone, commonly used for semi-precious coloured stones.

MORGANITE: Pink coloured beryl.

MUTTONFAT JADE: Whitish coloured nephrite.

NACRE: The fine surface layers of a pearl, or mother-of-pearl (which is the inside layer of the shell).

NATIVE-CUT: Stones cut at source, particularly in India and Sri Lanka.

NEPHRITE: Opaque stone varying from dark green to white, to brown, sometimes confused with jadeite as both are termed "jade".

NIELLO: Engraved design filled with a black metal alloy.

NON NUCLEATED: Freshwater cultured pearls which apparently have no core, the small piece of mantle originally inserted to start the nacreous process having dissolved before the pearl is formed completely.

OLIVINE: Mineral name for peridot.

ONYX: Brown and black chalcedony (agate).

OPALESCENCE: Flashes of rainbow colours seen against the milky background of white opals.

OPAQUE: Impervious to light.

OPEN BACKED: Form of setting jewellery where the stones can be seen from the reverse.

OPEN-WORK: Form of setting jewellery where stones are set in an open design determined by the metal, opposite of pavé setting.

PARCEL-GILT: Silver partly overlaid with gold.

PARIS JET: Black glass imitating jet.

PASTE: Jewellery set with glass instead of real stones.

PATE DE VERRE: Powdered glass, moulded, fired and enamelled lightly, a material used in art nouveau jewellery.

PAVÉ SET: Form of setting where the stones are adjacent to one another with the minimum of metal showing on the surface.

PAVILION: Lower part of a cut stone, below the girdle.

PECTORAL: Jewellery worn on the chest, usually associated with ancient jewellery.

PINCHBECK: Alloy of zinc and copper developed by Christopher Pinchbeck and used instead of gold in less expensive jewellery of the late 18th and early 19th centuries.

PIQUÉ WORK: The inlay of tortoiseshell with silver and gold in fine and intricate designs.

PLAQUE CUT: Cut in flat tablets, for engraving seals, etc.

PLAY OF COLOUR: Synonymous with iridescence and opalescence.

PLIQUE-A-JOUR: Form of enamelling when enamels are set in open metal frames, particularly popular with French art nouveau jewellery.

QUARTZ TOPAZ: Yellow or brown citrine (quartz), and not true topaz.

REFRACTIVE INDEX: Method of identifying a gemstone by measuring the angle at which the light rays are optically bent when entering a stone.

REPOUSSÉ: Metal which has been pushed into a raised design from the reverse.

ROSE DIAMONDS: Refers to the cut, and not their colour.

RUBELLITE: Red coloured tourmaline.

RUTILE: Mineral found in quartz, forming in long strands, when known as "Venus hair-stone".

SARDONYX: Banded form of chalcedony (agate).

SATSUMA: Japanese glazed earthenware, finely over-painted and gilded, particularly associated with the 18th and 19th centuries.

SCARABS: Beetles worn as amulets by the Egyptians, their form imitated in various materials such as faïence and cornelian. Also found in Roman jewellery.

SERPENTINE: An aggregate carved more frequently as objets d'art than jewellery, although bowenite is one kind which is used to simulate jade.

SHOULDERS: The top half of a ring shank, on either side of a "cluster" or single stone.

SILK: Whitish reflection or inclusion, seen particularly in sapphires and Burma rubies.

SOUDE: Triplet of quartz and green gelatine, usually simulating emerald.

SPECIFIC GRAVITY: Measurement of the density of gemstones, helpful as an identification test.

SPINACH JADE: Dark green spinach-coloured nephrite.

STEATITE: Soapstone, sometimes used to imitate pale-coloured jade.

STEP-CUT: Form of cutting in horizontal layered bands, used for coloured stones, identical to "emerald" and "trap" cuts.

STOMACHER: Large brooch worn centrally, usually pinned to the bodice of a dress, often made with detachable pendant sections and drops.

STOVE-ENAMELLED: Enamelling at very low temperature.

STRAPWORK: Formal geometrical banded designs of the Renaissance and 16th century.

STRASS: French jeweller who perfected the manufacture of white glass and developed high quality paste jewellery in the 18th century.

STYLE OF: In the manner of a known craftsman or artist, but unsigned or authenticated.

SUNSTONE: Spangled orange-yellow type of feldspar.

SWISS JADE: Green agate used to imitate jade.

SWISS LAPIS: Blue stained jaspar (agate).

SYNTHETIC: Gemstone of identical chemical composition as the natural stone but produced in the laboratory, whereas an imitation may be made of anything but look like the natural stone at first glance.

TABLE: Flat top facet of a brilliant- or step-cut stone.

TORQUE: Prehistoric Irish neck or wrist ornament.

TOUR A GUILLOCHER: See **BASSE TAILLE.**

TRANSLUCENT: Allowing light to pass through, but not transparent.

TRANSVAAL JADE: A dark green opaque form of grossular garnet which looks like jade.

TRAP-CUT: See **EMERALD-** and **STEP-CUT.**

TREMBLANT: Parts of a brooch set with a spring behind to give a shimmering effect and movement are said to be "en tremblant".

TRIPLETS: Three pieces of stone stuck together in layers to imitate a finer stone, e.g. triplet opals are made of a thin surface layer of flass or crystal covering a piece of black opal, and backed with opal matrix.

VAUXHALL GLASS: Black glass imitating jet, or coloured glass with a mirrored back.

VENUS HAIRSTONE: Rock crystal with long hair-like inclusion of reddish gold rutile.

VERNEUIL: Chemist who developed a process for the synthesis of corundum and spinel.

VERRE EGLOMISÉ: Glass which is painted from the reverse, usually with gold or black, popular in the Renaissance and 16th century.

VINAIGRETTE: Small container of silver or gold with a sponge soaked in aromatic vinegar to ward off evil smells.

WEDGWOOD: Staffordshire potter whose factory produced jasper-ware, blue, green and black with applied white decoration. In jewellery, popularly made as cameos in the late 18th and early 19th centuries in the neo-classical style.

WINDOWS: Directions of transparency and little colour in coloured stones, particularly sapphires.

Some Jewellers dealing in Antique and Second-Hand Jewellery in Great Britain

(Taken from *The Guide to the Antique Shops of Britain,* 1981 edition). Those who are Members of The British Antique Dealers' Association are asterisked * accordingly.)

LONDON

Antiquarius Antique Market, 135/141 King's Road, S.W.3. Tel. 351 2178.

Antique Hypermarket, 26-40 Kensington High Street, W.8. Tel. 937 1572.

Armour-Winston Ltd., 43 Burlington Arcade, W.1. Tel. 493 8937.

*Armytage Clarke, 9 Blenheim Street, W.1. Tel. 629 0308.

*Asprey & Co. Ltd., 165-169 New Bond Street, W.1. Tel. 493 6767.

C. Barnett & Co., 51 Burlington Arcade, W.1. Tel. 493 2570.

Bentley & Co., 65 New Bond Street, W.1. Tel. 629 0651/0325.

Bermondsey Antique Market Ltd., 241/255 Long Lane, Bermondsey, S.E.1. Tel. 937 1572.

N. Bloom & Son (Antiques) Ltd., 40/41 Conduit Street, W.1. Tel. 629 5060.

Bond Street Antique Centre, 124 New Bond Street, W.1. Tel. 937 1572.

*Cameo Corner Ltd., 22 New Bond Street, W.1. Tel. 629 0071.

*Carrington & Co. Ltd., 25 Old Bond Street, W.1. Tel. 734 3727.

*Collingwood of Conduit Street Ltd., 46 Conduit Street, W.1. Tel. 734 2656.

A.B. Davis, 18 Brook Street, W.1. Tel. 629 1053.

Delehar, 146 Portobello Road, W.11. Tel. 727 9860.

*M. Ekstein Ltd., 90 Jermyn Street, S.W.1. Tel. 930 2024.

The Fleamarket, 7 Pierrepont Row, Camden Passage, Islington, N.1. Tel. 226 6627.

*Garrard & Co. Ltd., 112 Regent Street, W.1. Tel. 734 7020.

*Nicholas Gorevic, 97 Jermyn Street, S.W.1. Tel. 930 1589.

*Gowland Brothers Ltd., 48 Cornhill, E.C.3. Tel. 626 9155.

Green's Antique Galleries, 117 Kensington Church Street, W.8. Tel. 229 9618.

*M. Hakim, 4 The Royal Arcade, Old Bond Street, W.1. Tel. 629 2643.

*Hancocks & Co. (Jewellers) Ltd., 1 Burlington Gardens, W.1. Tel. 493 8904.

*Harris (Antiques) Ltd., 5 Hatton Garden, E.C.1. Tel. 405 2751.

Harris & Frank Limited, 53 Holland Park, W.11. Tel. 727 4769.

*Harvey & Gore (Antiques) Ltd., 4 Burlington Gardens, W.1. Tel. 493 2714.

*Hennell Ltd., 1 Davies Street, W.1. Tel. 493 3011.

*Holmes Ltd., 29 Old Bond Street, W.1. Tel. 493 1396.

J.I. Horwhit (H. Faber Ltd.), 94 Southampton Row, W.C.1. Tel. 405 0749.

The Jewel House Ltd., 35 Sloane Street, S.W.1. Tel. 235 6325.

*Johnson Walker & Tolhurst Ltd., 21 Conduit Street, W.1. Tel. 629 2615.

H. Knowles-Brown Ltd., 27 Hampstead High Street, N.W.3. Tel. 435 4775.

* S. Lampard & Son Ltd., 32 Notting Hill Gate, W.11. Tel. 229 5457.

*D.S. Lavender, 63 South Molton Street, W.1. Tel. 629 1782.

*Liberty & Co. Ltd., Regent Street, W.1. Tel. 734 1234.

*James R. Ogden & Sons Ltd., 42 Duke Street, St. James's, S.W.1. Tel. 930 3353.

*Richard Ogden Ltd., 28-29 Burlington Arcade, W.1. Tel. 493 9136.

Pearl Cross Ltd., 35 St. Martin's Court, W.C.2. Tel. 836 2814.

*S.J. Phillips Ltd., 139 New Bond Street, W.1. Tel. 629 6261.

Searle & Co. Ltd., 1 Royal Exchange, E.C.2. Tel. 626 2456.

*Shapland, 207 High Holborn, W.C.1. Tel. 405 3507.

*Tessiers Ltd., 26 New Bond Street, W.1. Tel. 629 0458.

Tortoiseshell & Ivory House Ltd., 24 Chiltern Street, W.1. Tel. 935 8031.

*Wartski (Jewellers) Ltd., 14 Grafton Street, W.1. Tel. 493 1141.

OUTSIDE LONDON

AVON
Bath: *D. & B. Dickinson, 22 New Bond Street. Tel. 66502.

*C.T. Gilmer Ltd., 16/17 Old Bond Street. Tel. 66754.

*E.P. Mallory & Son Ltd., 1-4 Bridge Street. Tel. 65885.

Bristol: Grey-Harris & Co., 12 Princess Street, Clifton. Tel. 37365.

The Mall Antique Galleries, 34/36 The Mall, Clifton. Tel. 30358.

Quinneys, 17 The Mall. Tel. 35877; 54 Park Row. Tel. 23555.

BEDFORDSHIRE
Luton: Kay's Corner, 156 Biscot Road. Tel. 26491.

Leaside Antiques, 44 Gordon Street. Tel. 27957.

BERKSHIRE
Maidenhead: Lowe & Pomfrett Ltd., 63 Queen Street. Tel. 20759.

CAMBRIDGESHIRE
Cambridge: Hilton Gallery, 3 St. Mary's Passage. Tel. 356886.

Wisbech: * Peter A. Crofts, Briar Patch, High Road, Elm. Tel. 4614.

CHESHIRE
Chester: Lowe & Sons, 11 Bridge Street Row. Tel. 25850.

Hale: Anne Kerr Antiques, 191a Ashley Road. Tel. 061 928 0091.

Reddish: G.E. Leigh & Son, Houldsworth Square. Tel. 061 432 2413.

CORNWALL
Lostwithiel: Mary Farrant Antiques, 22 Queen Street. Tel. 872227.

Padstow: Mayflower Antiques, 2 Mill Road. Tel. 532308.

Truro: Alan Bennett, 15/16 St. Mary's Street. Tel. 3296.

DERBYSHIRE
Derby: F.H. Pratt, 11 Friar Gate. Tel. 43003.

DEVON
Exeter: *William Bruford & Son Ltd., 1 Bedford Street. Tel. 54901.

John Nathan Antiques, 153/154 Cowick Street, St. Thomas. Tel. 72228.

Sidmouth: Copperfields, 1 Church Street. Tel. 2145.

Torquay: Enid Seaman, 266 Union Street, Torre. Tel. 22184.

DORSET
Bournemouth: Shippey's (Boscombe) Ltd., 15/16 Royal Arcade, Boscombe. Tel. 36548.

DURHAM
Darlington: *Ronald S. Richardson, 6/7 Post House, Wynd. Tel. 64860.

ESSEX
Castle Hedingham: Orbell House Gallery, Orbell House. Tel. Hedingham 60298.

Colchester: F.R. Cooper & Son, Trinity Square. Tel. 72968.

GLOUCESTERSHIRE
Cheltenham: Bick, 5 Montpellier Walk. Tel. 24738.

*Martin & Co. Ltd., 19 The Promenade. Tel. 22821.

*Scott-Cooper Ltd., 52 The Promenade. Tel. 22580.

Cirencester: Walter Bull & Son (Cirencester) Ltd., 10 Dyer Street. Tel. 3875.

GREATER LONDON
Sutton: S. Warrender & Co., 4 Cheam Road. Tel. 01 643 4381.

HAMPSHIRE
Portsmouth: *A. Fleming (Southsea) Ltd., Clock Tower, Castle Road. Tel. 22934.

Leslie's, 107 Fratton Road. Tel. 25952.

HERTFORDSHIRE
Berkhamsted: F.E. Norwood Ltd., 146 High Street. Tel. 4361.

St. Albans: Josephine Grahame-Ballin, 21 George Street. Tel. 56069.

LANCASHIRE
Ashton-under-Lyne: *Kenworthy's Ltd., 226 Stamford Street. Tel. 061 330 3043.

Lancaster: Ann Tique, Curio Jewellers, 73 North Road. Tel. 65343.

Manchester: Butter Lane Antique Centre, 40a King Street West. Tel. 061 834 1809.

*E. & C.T. Koopman & Son Ltd., John Dalton House, 4 John Dalton Street. Tel. 061 834 2420.

LINCOLNSHIRE
Woodhall Spa: *James Best (Antiques) Ltd., The Broadway. Tel. 52513.

NORFOLK
Cromer: Bond Street Antiques, 6 Bond Street. Tel. 513134.

Great Yarmouth: Peter Howkins, 39, 40 & 135 King Street. Tel. 4639.

Norwich: Charles Cubitt, 10 All Saints Green. Tel. 22569.

*Henry Levine & Co., 55 London Street. Tel. 28709.

NORTHAMPTONSHIRE
Wellingborough: Croyland Antiques, 26a Sheep Street. Tel. 223370.

NOTTINGHAMSHIRE
Nottingham: M. Kemp, 88-91 Derby Road. Tel. 47055.

Twemlow & Co. Ltd., 17 King Street. Tel. 42677.

OXFORDSHIRE
Oxford: *The Antiquary, 50 St. Giles's Street. Tel. 59875.

*Reginald Davis, 34 High Street. Tel. 48347.

*Payne & Son (Goldsmiths) Ltd., 131 High Street. Tel. 43787.

*Rowell & Son Ltd., 115 High Street. Tel. 42187.

SHROPSHIRE

Shrewsbury: The Little Gem, 18 St. Mary's Street. Tel. 52085.

SOMERSET

Taunton: Bath Place Antiques, 9 Bath Place. Tel. 85050.

Wells: *Edward A. Nowell, 21/23 Market Place. Tel. 72415.

SURREY

Dorking: Eleanor Hutton, 59 West Street. Tel. 883777.

Redhill: S. Warrender & Co., 57 High Street. Tel. 64006.

SUSSEX

Brighton: Connoisseur Antiques, 59 Ship Street. Tel. 29190.

D.H. Edmonds, 27 and 28 Meeting House Lane. Tel. 27713.

Eastbourne: *Wm. Bruford & Son Ltd., 60/62 Terminus Road. Tel. 25452.

Lewes: *Stephen Moore Ltd., Castle Place, 166 High Street. Tel. 4158.

Petworth: *Ernest Streeter & Daughter, The Clock House, Church Street. Tel. 42239.

Westbourne: Westbourne Antiques, 1 Lamb Buildings, The Square. Tel. Emsworth 3711.

Worthing: Cameo Corner, 163 Montague Street. Tel. 30533.

TYNE & WEAR

Newcastle-upon-Tyne: Davidson's The Jewellers Ltd., 94/96 Grey Street. Tel. 22551.

S. & R. Antiques, 13 High Bridge, Bigg Market. Tel. 26739.

WARWICKSHIRE

Stratford-upon-Avon: Jim Barnett, 32 Meer Street. Tel. 66019.

Warwick: * A.T. Silvester & Son Ltd., 2/4 High Street. Tel. 42972.

WEST MIDLANDS

Birmingham: *D. & M. Davis Ltd., 3 Livery Street. Tel. 021 236 1304.

*Perry Greaves Ltd., 1 Corporation Street. Tel. 021 643 5479.

Nathan & Co. (Birmingham) Ltd., 31 Corporation Street. Tel. 021 643 5225.

YORKSHIRE

Bradford: Langley's (Jewellers) Ltd., 59 Godwin Street. Tel. 22280.

Harrogate: *W.F. Greenwood & Sons Ltd., 2/3 Crown Place. Tel. 504467.

*James R. Ogden & Sons Ltd., 38 St. James Street. Tel. 504123.

*Christopher Warner, 15 Princes Street. Tel. 503617.

Huddersfield: Fillans (Antiques), 2 Market Walk. Tel. 20889.

Settle: Mary Milnthorpe – Antiques, Antique Shop, Market Place. Tel. 2331.

Sheffield: H. Hayden, 477 London Road. Tel. 56998.

Shipley. *Bethell Antiques, 149 Bradford Road. Tel. 581318.

York: *W.F. Greenwood & Sons Ltd., 37 Stonegate. Tel. 23864.

R.K. Himsworth, 28 The Shambles. Tel. 25089.

SCOTLAND

AYRSHIRE

Ayr: Allan Antiques, 24 Parkhouse Street. Tel. 65486.

LANARKSHIRE

Glasgow: James Forrest & Co. (Jewellers) Ltd., 105 West Nile Street. Tel. 041 332 0494.

H. Lyons & Son, 61 West Regent Street. Tel. 041 332 1833.

Thornton Taylor Antiques, 2c Fernleigh Road. Tel. 041 637 7749.

MIDLOTHIAN

Edinburgh: H. Chernack, 85/87 Rose Street. Tel. 031 225 3038.

Goodwin's Antiques, 17a Queensferry Street. Tel. 031 225 4717.

John White, 116b Rose Street. Tel. 031 225 2140.

Wildman Bros., 54 Hanover Street. Tel. 031 225 6754.

PERTHSHIRE

Perth: Henderson, 5 North Methven Street. Tel. 24836.

NORTHERN IRELAND

CO. ANTRIM

Newtownabbey: *New Abbey Antiques, Caragh Lodge, Glen Road. Tel. Whiteabbey 62036.

CO. ARMAGH

Armagh: J.A. Johnston (Jewellers) Ltd., 29 English Street. Tel. 522753.

Suggested Further Reading

ALDRED, Cyril. *Jewels of the Pharaohs*. Thames & Hudson Ltd., London, 1971.

AMAYA, M. *Art Nouveau*. London, 1966.

ANTIQUE COLLECTORS' CLUB. *Guide to the Antique Shops of Britain*, annually.

ARMSTRONG, Nancy. *Jewellery, an Historical Survey of British Styles and Jewels*. London, 1973.

BALL, S.H. *A Roman Book on Precious Stones*. Los Angeles, 1951.

BECK, R.J., REED, A.H. and REED, A.W. *New Zealand Jade: the Story of Greenstone*. Wellington, New Zealand, 1971.

BENNETT, E.M. *Turquoise and the Indian*. Chicago, 1970.

BLAKEMORE, K. *Collecting Gems and Ornamental Stones*. London, 1966.

BOARDMAN, J. *Engraved Gems*. London, 1968.

BRUTON, E. *The True Book about Diamonds*. London, 1961.

CHALMERS, R.O. *Australian Rocks, Minerals and Gemstones*. Sydney, 1966.

CLIFFORD, Anne. *Cut-Steel and Berlin Iron Jewellery*. Bath, England, 1971.

COOPER, C.W. *The Precious Stones of the Bible*. London, 1924.

CURRAN, M. *Jewels and Gems*. London, 1961.

DICKENSON, J.Y. *The Book of Pearls*. New York, 1968.

DOUGHTY, O. *Early Diamond Days: The Opening of the Diamond Fields of South Africa*. London, 1963.

EVANS, Joan. *English Jewellery from the Fifth Century to 1800*. Methuen, London, 1921. *Magical Jewels of the Middle Ages and the Renaissance*. Oxford, 1922. *A History of Jewellery, 1100-1870* (contains very full bibliography). London and New York, 1923; rev. ed. London, 1970.

EVANS, I.O. *Rocks, Minerals and Gemstones*. London, 1971.

EYLES, W.C. *The Book of Opals*. U.S.A. and Japan, 1964.

FALKINER, Richard. *Investing in Antique Jewellery*. Barrie and Jenkins.

FLOWER, Margaret. *Victorian Jewellery*. London and New York, 1951; rev. ed. London 1967.

GERE, Charlotte. *Victorian Jewellery Design*. London, 1972. *European and American Jewellery 1830-1914*. London, 1975.

GERLACH, Martin. *Primitive and Folk Jewellery*. Edited by Martin Gerlach, Dover Books. (A re-issue of a German work of 1906.)

HIGGINS, R.A. *Greek and Roman Jewellery*. London, 1961.

HOFFMANN, H. and DAVIDSON, P.F. *Greek Gold*. Brooklyn Museum, 1965.

HUGHES, G. *Modern Jewelry*. London, 1963; 2nd ed. 1964. *The Art of Jewelry*. London, 1972.

JESSUP, Ronald. *Anglo-Saxon Jewellery*. Faber & Faber, London, 1950.

KAGAN, Ju. *Western European Cameos in the Hermitage Collection*. Aurora Art Publishers, Leningrad, 1973.

LEECHMAN, F. *The Opal Book*. Sydney, 1961.

LEWIS, M.D.S. *Antique Paste Jewellery*. London, 1970.

MARSHALL, F.H. *Catalogue of the Jewellery, Greek, Etruscan and Roman in the British Museum*. London, 1911. *Catalogue of Finger Rings, Greek, Etruscan and Roman in the British Museum*.

MAXWELL-HYSLOP, K.R. *Western Asiatic Jewellery*. Methuen.

NAYLOR, Gillian. *The Arts and Crafts Movement*. London, 1971.

NOTT, S.C. *Chinese Jade Throughout the Ages*. London, 1937.

OMAN, C.C. *Victoria and Albert Museum Catalogue of Rings, 1930. Rings*.

PERRY, N. and PERRY, R. *Australian Gemstones in Colour*. Sydney, 1967.

PETER, Mary. *Collecting Victorian Jewellery*. London, 1970.

POGUE, J.E. *The Turquoise*. Washington, D.C., 1915; reprinted with additions, New Mexico, 1973.

QUICK, L. *The Book of Agates*. London, 1963.

ROSS, M.C. *Fabergé and his Contemporaries*. Cleveland Museum of Art, 1965.

RUTLAND, E.H. *An Introduction to the Gemstones of the World*. London and U.S.A., 1974.

SITWELL, H.D.W. *The Crown Jewels*. London, 1953.

SNOWMAN, K. *The Art of Carl Fabergé*. London, 1953.

SOTHEBY. *Guilhou Collection of Rings*. 9 November, 1937.

WEBSTER, Robert. *Gems*. London, 1975.

WILKINSON, Alex. *Ancient Egyptian Jewellery*. Methuen.

WILLIAMSON, C.G. *The Book of Amber*. London, 1932.